101
Fairy Things
to make
and do

igloobooks
.com

Published in 2012
by Igloo Books Ltd
Cottage Farm
Sywell
NN6 0BJ
www.igloobooks.com

Copyright © 2012 Igloo Books Ltd

HUN001 0912
4 6 8 10 9 7 5 3
ISBN: 978-0-85780-306-1

Illustrated by Paula Doherty

Printed and manufactured in China

Contents

Chapter 1
Fairy Fashion

From the tips of their shimmery wings to the ends of their glittery shoes, fairies always like to look beautiful. If you look out for pretty pieces of scrap fabric, artificial flowers, colorful ribbons and bows, sparkly beads, buttons and stick-on jewels in all sorts of candy colors, you'll be able to make the prettiest fairy jewellery, headdresses and hair accessories, as well as flowery skirts, tutus and fairy wings.

Why not match your fashion accessories to the colors of your favorite fairy—using shades of blue and turquoise for Bluebell Sapphire and yellow, orange and gold shades for Amber Lily?

Fairy Flowers

Fairies love flowers. They use them to decorate their surroundings and they wear them in their hair and on their clothes. It's fun to pick your own fresh flowers and leaves from the garden and hedgerows, but always check with an adult first.

Daisy Chain

1 Pick some daisies, making sure the stems are as long as possible. Using your thumbnail, make a vertical slit halfway along the stem of the first daisy. Thread the stem of another daisy through the hole.

2 Make a slit in the stem of the second daisy and then thread another daisy stem through it. Keep doing this until you have used up all of your daisies and then join the ends together. You can wear your daisy chain around your neck or on your head like a garland.

You could also make a pretty chain with other garden flowers such as buttercups.

Wear a flower in your hair

Pick a flower – a rose, marguerite, dahlia, pansy or clematis work well. Cut its stem short, then wear it in your hair like our fairy friends. Put your hair in bunches or a ponytail and poke the flower stem into it, near the hair band. Secure the flower in place with a couple of grips.

Daisy Pearl says:
'When you pick a flower, try and keep the stem as long as possible to make it easier when you are threading the daisies.'

Jasmine Emerald's Hairclip

1 Trace the circle and petal shapes using the templates at the bottom of this page onto a piece of paper. Ask an adult to help you cut out the templates and use them to cut out 16 petals and 2 circles from your fabric scraps.

YOU WILL NEED
Tracing paper and pencil
Piece of paper
Scraps of fabric
Fabric glue
Bead or button
Hair slide

2 Glue the ends of half your petals onto the circle to make a flower shape, overlapping the petals as you go.

3 Glue the other half of the petals onto the other circle in the same way.

4 Glue the two circles together, making sure that the petals on the back flower can be seen between the ones on the front flower.

5 Glue a button or bead into the center of the top circle and then glue the flower onto your hair slide.

Templates
Circle and petal templates for
Jasmine Emerald's Hairclip

Pretty Flower Headband

Bluebell Sapphire loves to wear lots of bright colors, especially in her hair. Why not make a lovely headband decorated with pretty flowers to wear to birthday parties? Ask an adult to help you thread the flowers onto your headband.

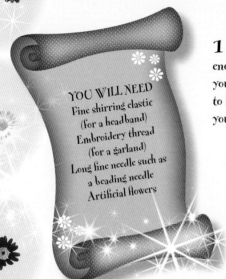

YOU WILL NEED
Fine shirring elastic
(for a headband)
Embroidery thread
(for a garland)
Long fine needle such as
a beading needle
Artificial flowers

1 Cut a piece of elastic, long enough to fit comfortably around your head, with a little extra to knot the ends together when you've finished.

2 Ask an adult to help you thread the elastic through the eye of a needle. Push the needle through the base of a flower and push it about 10–15cm (4–6in) from the end of the elastic.

3 Thread more flowers by pushing them down the length of the elastic and leaving an equal gap between each one.

Flower Garland

Use some embroidery thread in a color that matches your flowers, or use green thread, like flower stems. Cut a length of embroidery thread long enough to make a garland to wear around your neck and thread on the flowers as instructed above. If you need to, tie a knot under each flower to hold it in place.

4 Tie the ends of the elastic together and wear the band around your head with the knot under your hair at the back.

8

Ribbon Rose Corsage

Ruby Rose's favorite flowers are roses. Here's how to make a gorgeous rose using a wire-edged ribbon. You can pin it to your coat lapel or sweater, near your shoulder. You could also pin it onto a cushion.

YOU WILL NEED
50cm (20in) wire-edged ribbon, approximately 4cm(1½in) wide
Fabric glue
Large safety pin

1 Pull about 1cm (⅓in) of wire out at one end of the ribbon and bend it over to secure. Pull the other end of the same wire, pushing the fabric away to gather up one edge of the ribbon and creating a tail of wire.

2 Starting at the first end, with the 1cm (⅓in) of wire, tightly roll up the gathered edge of the ribbon, adjusting the flower shape as you go. Add dabs of glue along the gathered edge as you roll to secure the base of the flower.

3 When your flower is complete, wind the tail of wire tightly around the base of your rose to secure it. Make sure any sharp ends are tucked in.

Rosebud Accessories

Use narrower ribbon and make several small rosebuds. You can then stick these onto a plastic Alice band or hair slide using some craft glue.

4 Take a large safety pin and ask an adult to help you push it through the base of your flower. Pin the corsage onto your clothes.

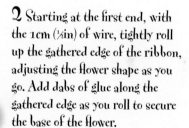

Pretty Twirling Tutu

This gorgeous tutu will make you want to dance and twirl around like a fairy. You can use up to four different colors of tulle for your tutu or make it all in one color. Wear it over a leotard and tights.

1 Put the ribbon around your waist and tie a knot at each end where the ribbons meet, making sure you leave an equal amount at either end for the waist ties (at least 25cm/10in).

YOU WILL NEED
150cm (60in) satin ribbon
1m (3ft 3in) of four different colors of tulle fabric
Tape measure
Dressmaking scissors

2 Spread out each piece of tulle on the floor and loosely roll it up.

Top Tip!
If you love everything sparkly, you can decorate your tutu with shiny rhinestones, jewels and sequins, fixing them in place with fabric glue. You could also tie some lengths of ribbon in between the strips of tulle.

3 Ask an adult to help you trim off the ragged ends and then cut the rolled-up fabric into pieces of about 8–10cm (3–4in). You should get about 15–20 strips per meter of tulle, depending on the width of the fabric. Repeat Steps 2 and 3 for all of the tulle.

4 Lay the ribbon waistband on your work surface. Unroll a strip of tulle and fold it in half. Put the loop behind the ribbon and feed the ends through the loop. Pull it tight to tie the tulle onto the ribbon.

5 Tie a few more strips of tulle onto your ribbon and then push them up against the left-hand knot.

6 Continue in this way until you have filled the ribbon between the knots with strips of tulle, alternating colors as you wish.

7 Put the tutu around your waist and fasten it with a bow at the front or back.

Fairy Pom-pom

Take a strip of tulle and punch holes along one long side with a hole-puncher, spacing them evenly. Thread a length of thin ribbon in and out of the holes, all the way along. Pull both ends of the ribbon tight to gather up the tulle in the center. Tie a knot in the ribbon and, there you have it, a fairy pom-pom! If you wish, you can decorate your pom-pom by sticking sequins all over it.

You can tie your pom-pom around your wrist, waist or head, or just knot the ends of the ribbon and swing it from your arm. Alternatively, glue it onto the end of a wooden skewer covered with kitchen foil to make a pom-pom wand.

Flower Petal Skirt

This lovely skirt is perfect for dressing up in. It's made up of overlapping fabric 'petals' glued onto a length of cotton tape. You can make all your petals out of the same fabric or use different colors and patterns. It's a great way to use up old scraps of fabric.

YOU WILL NEED
Paper for pattern
Pins
8 pieces of fabric, large enough to fit your template
Pinking shears
150cm (60in) cotton tape, 4cm (1½in) wide
Fabric glue

1 Trace the petal template at the bottom of this page onto a piece of paper, making it the length you want your skirt to be and 20cm (8in) wide at the top. Then, ask an adult to help you cut out the paper template.

2 Pin the paper template onto your piece of fabric and ask an adult to cut around it with pinking shears. Cut out eight petals.

3 Measure 25cm (10in) along your tape and mark this point with a pencil – this is the skirt tie.

4 Apply fabric glue to the wrong side of the top edge of your first petal and stick it onto the tape, aligning the edge with the mark on the tape.

10cm

Template

Enlarge this template so that it is long enough to reach from your waist to your knees. You can, of course, make your skirt longer or shorter.

5 Measure 10cm (4in) along the first petal and mark this point with a pencil. Stick the next petal in place on the tape, aligning the edge with the mark so that it overlaps half of the first petal.

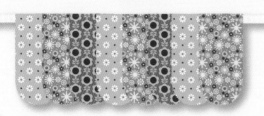

6 Stick the rest of the petals on in the same way, overlapping each one with half of the next one. You will end up with another 25cm (10in) of tape, which will be the other tie.

7 Hold onto one tie and wrap the skirt around your waist. Then tie the ends of the tape together in a bow. Wear your petal skirt over leggings or tights.

Enchanting Mask

Make a gorgeous fairy mask to wear with your tutu or petal skirt and fairy wings. Decorate it with all things sparkly and colorful.

1 Trace the outline of the mask onto the card using the template shown below. Ask an adult to cut out the mask and make a hole in each side for the elastic.

YOU WILL NEED
Tracing paper and pencil
Piece of card,
15 x 20cm (6 x 8in)
Glitter and feathers
Craft glue
30cm (12in) thin elastic

2 Decorate the front of your mask by gluing on colorful glitter and feathers. Glue some feathers around the edge.

3 Thread the elastic through one hole from the front to the back and knot the end. Ask an adult to help you work out how tight you want the elastic to be around the back of your head and trim the other end to length. Thread it through the hole and knot the end.

Template

Enlarge the mask template to fit comfortably across your face. (You will want the holes at the sides to reach your ears.)

Dazzling Jewels

Fairies are always on the lookout for pretty beads, buttons and brooches that they can make into lovely necklaces and bracelets. Ask a family member whether they've got any old bits and pieces that you think a fairy would love and see what you can make out of them.

Glitter Pasta Necklace

YOU WILL NEED
Scrap paper
Dried pasta with holes
(penne or macaroni
work well)
Paint and paintbrush
Fine glitter in
different colors
Craft glue
String or embroidery thread
Tape

1 If you wish to paint some or all of your pasta, work on scrap paper and paint your pasta pieces with a paintbrush, and leave them to dry.

2 Pour some glitter onto clean scrap paper. Use a different piece of paper for each color of glitter.

3 Apply glue to your pasta shapes and roll them in the glitter. You can coat them all in glitter or make patterns. Leave the glitter to dry thoroughly.

4 Ask an adult to cut a piece of string or thread to the length you want your necklace to be, plus an extra 15cm (6in) so that you can knot the ends. Make sure it will go over your head easily.

5 Tape one end of the string or thread to your work surface so that the pasta pieces can't slip off. Start threading on your pasta shapes, alternating colors as you wish.

6 Tie the ends of the string or thread together securely and trim the ends.

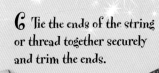

Pretty Beads

YOU WILL NEED
Beading wire
Selection of sparkly beads,
such as seed beads and
bugle beads

1 Ask an adult to cut a piece of beading wire to the required length. Thread on the first bead and make a loop at one end so that the beads won't fall off. Do this by bending up the end and twisting the loop a couple of times.

2 Have fun building up your design, threading on the prettiest beads in the colors you think your fairy friends would choose.

3 When you've finished, being very careful not to let the beads slip off the end, twist the two ends very tightly together a few times to secure them. Ask an adult to help you trim the ends of the wire.

Violet Amethyst loves rich purples and oh-so-pretty lilacs and mauves.

Ruby Rose prefers all the shades of pink and red.

Good Luck Charm

YOU WILL NEED
6 large beads or buttons
3 pieces of cord or doubled
embroidery thread,
10cm (4in) long
1 piece of cord or fine ribbon,
long enough for a necklace

1 Thread a bead onto a length of cord or doubled embroidery thread and knot it securely at one end. Thread another bead onto the other end of the same thread and knot it securely. Repeat for the other two threads. Make sure the knots are tight and then trim the ends.

2 Lay the three beaded threads one above the other so the beads line up with each other. Thread the long piece of cord or ribbon under the center of the three cords. Center it and tie the ends together in a tight knot.

3 Knot the other ends of the ribbon together and put it over your head.

Friends Forever Bracelet

1 Lay the strands on your work surface in matching pairs. Fold them all in half together and tie a knot to make a loop about 3.5cm (1½in) long.

2 Tape the loop to your work surface or ask your friend to hold it. Separate the strands into three colored sections – pink, blue and yellow – and start plaiting.

3 Once you have a plait that will fit your wrist, split the middle strand in half to make two strands instead of three, and knot them together.

4 Separate each of these two strands into three and plait each one to make two mini plaits. Knot the ends of each plait.

5 Put the bracelet around your friend's wrist. Put one small plait through the loop and knot the small plaits together.

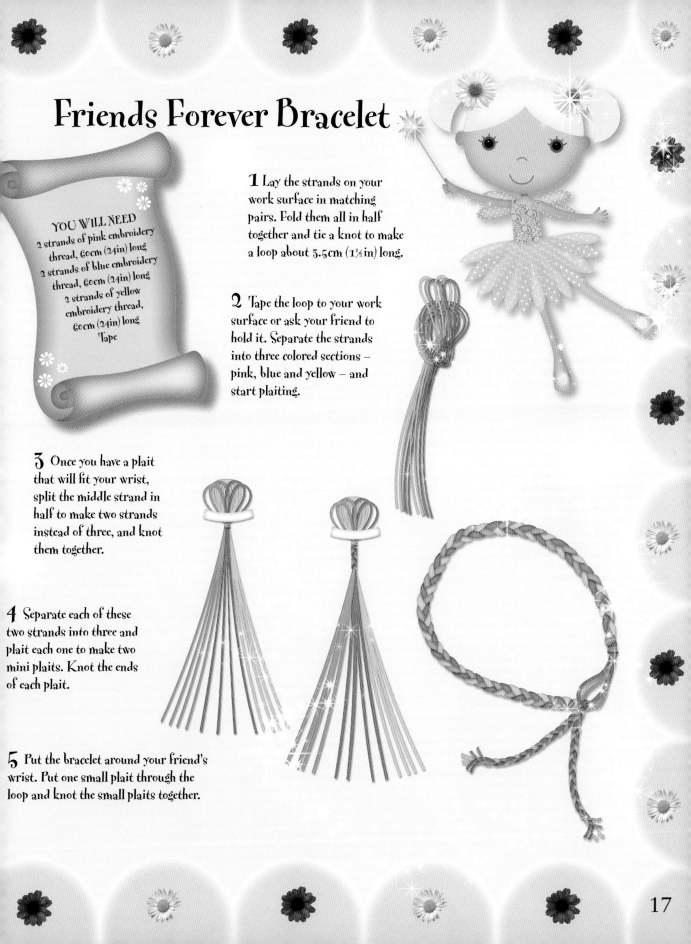

Fairy Headdresses

Have fun creating these beautiful headdresses and sparkle like a Queen, or Princess. You will find your magic works even better when you're wearing one.

Fairy Queen's Crown

YOU WILL NEED
Tracing paper and pencil
Purple card
Sequins, jewels, glitter and glue or stickers to decorate
Shirring elastic

1 Trace the crown shape shown below onto a piece of card. Ask an adult to help you cut out the crown and make two small holes in each bottom corner.

2 Decorate your crown by sticking sparkly jewels, sequins, or stickers all over the front.

3 Ask an adult to help you tie a length of elastic through one of the holes. Then, ask them to hold the crown in place and help you tie the other end of the elastic through the second hole, to secure the crown.

Fairy Princess' Tiara

1 Ask an adult to cut some strips of foil 2.5cm (1in) wide. Wrap your Alice band with foil strips until it is completely covered, sticking down the ends with a dab of glue.

2 Lay a strip of foil shiny side down and fold both long edges in to the center so they meet. Fold the strip in half again. Ask an adult to cut the foil into strips, one strip to be 13cm (5in) long and six strips 10cm (4in) long.

3 Bring the ends of each strip together and glue them to make a loop.

4 Stick the ends of the large loop to the Alice band in the center, so the loop is sticking up.

5 Stick the ends of the six smaller loops on either side of the central one, overlapping them. Then decorate your tiara with sequins and jewels.

YOU WILL NEED
Kitchen foil
Thin Alice band
Craft glue
Sequins, jewels and glue
or stickers to decorate

Top Tip!

You can also glue jewels and sequins onto your hair slides and butterfly clips to make lovely, sparkly and colorful decorations that any fairy would love to wear.

Bejewelled Headband

Use a wide Alice band and a selection of stick-on jewels and rhinestones. If you have different shapes, work out a design for your jewels on your work surface first. Start in the center and work outwards, making the design symmetrical and alternating colors and shapes. Stick the first jewel in the center of your Alice band, then continue taking beads from your design and stick them in place on the Alice band.

Flower Crown

1 The base for this lovely crown is made in a similar way to the Spell Bells on page 25. You can collect all sorts of lovely woodland treasures to decorate your crown – such as flowers, leaves, little pine cones and feathers.

2 How many pipe cleaners you use will depend on their length. First make a crown out of a single layer of pipe cleaners by twisting the ends together to form a circle large enough to fit your head. If you have long pipe cleaners, just join two and bend them into a circle and twist the ends together. If you need to, join four pipe cleaners together first before bending them into a circle and joining the ends.

3 Twist more pipe cleaners around and around your first circle to make it double the thickness and strength. Tuck in all the ends neatly and tape them down using metallic tape.

4 Decorate your crown with the flowers, leaves, feathers and other treasures you have found, tucking them between the pipe cleaners and gluing them in place.

Top Tip!
If you can't get outside to collect your woodland treasures, make some colorful flowers out of scrunched-up tissue paper and glue those onto your crown. You could draw leaves onto green paper, cut them out and stick those on, too!

Beaded Headdresses

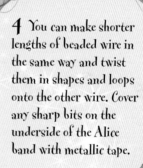

1 Ask an adult to cut a length of beading wire long enough to wind all the way around your Alice band. Leaving a 5cm (2in) tail, bend a loop at one end of the wire and twist it tightly.

2 Thread colorful beads onto the other end of the wire. When you have finished threading on the beads, bend another loop and twist it tightly to hold the beads in place.

3 Wrap the beaded wire around your Alice band. Secure the ends to the ends of the Alice band by sticking them down with metallic tape.

4 You can make shorter lengths of beaded wire in the same way and twist them in shapes and loops onto the other wire. Cover any sharp bits on the underside of the Alice band with metallic tape.

Sparkly Tinsel Twists

1 Take a gold pipe cleaner and fold it in half. Put it around the center of the Alice band and twist the ends together on top of the band.

2 Do the same with a silver pipe cleaner, securing it next to the gold pipe cleaner by twisting the ends together.

3 Add as many more gold and silver pipe cleaners as you wish along the top part of your Alice band. Bend the ends of the pipe cleaners as you wish, so they look like sparkly twigs.

Fairy Hair Accessories

As well as wearing flowers in their hair, fairies love to wear ribbons, bows, bobbles and all kinds of sparkly delights.

Sparkly Clips and Bands

YOU WILL NEED
Alice bands, hair slides
and butterfly clips
Craft glue
Scrap paper
Stick-on jewels
Ribbons
Artificial flowers
Beading wire and
colorful beads

1 Pour some fine glitter onto a piece of scrap paper. Paint craft glue onto a plastic Alice band or hair slide. Press the gluey side onto the glitter to coat it. Leave it to dry.

2 Use stick-on jewels to decorate plastic Alice bands, hair slides or butterfly clips.

3 Wrap your Alice band with colorful ribbons and stick the ends in place with a dab of craft glue.

4 If you have a velvet Alice band, glue artificial flowers or homemade ribbon rosebuds onto it.

5 Attach one end of a strand of beading wire to the base of a hair slide. Thread the wire with sparkly, colorful beads. Secure the end so that the beads can't fall off, and then wrap the beaded wire around the top part of the hair slide and secure at the other end of the hair slide.

Fairy Hair Bobbles

1 Take a strand of embroidery thread about 20cm (8in) long and tape one end to your work surface.

2 Thread a handful of large beads, sequins or buttons onto the thread.

3 Remove the tape and hold both ends of the thread so that the beads fall to the middle.

4 Knot the ends of the thread together tightly to make a 'bobble' of your beads, sequins or buttons. Tie the ends tightly around your ponytail band to attach the bobble and ask an adult to trim the ends of the thread.

Pretty Bows

Choose some lovely wide ribbon and tie it in a bow. You will need about 50cm (20in), depending on how large you want your bow to be. Ask an adult to trim the ends of the ribbon into a V-shape so that they don't fray. Glue the base of your bow onto a hair slide.

You could also use a length of ribbon as a headband. Put it around your head, across your forehead, and knot it at the back, leaving the tails hanging down over your hair. Or, put the ribbon under your hair at the back and tie it in a bow on top of your head.

Rainbow Ribbons

1 Align the ends of the ribbons and measure 25cm (10in) from one end. Knot the three ribbons together at this point.

2 Tape the ribbons to your work surface, just above the knot, to hold it still and plait the three ribbons together, bringing the left and right ribbon in turn over the central ribbon.

3 When you have plaited about 50cm (20in) of ribbon, tie another knot in the ribbons to secure the plait.

4 Untape the other end of the ribbon and tie the headband around your head. Leave the ends of the ribbons trailing down.

Fluttery Wings

This is an easy way to make fairy wings and you can have fun decorating them with glitter, sequins, jewels, ribbons or feathers.

1 Ask an adult to cut the hooks off the coat hangers using the wire cutters, just to where the wire twists on the neck of the hanger. Pull out the base of each coat hanger to make the wing shapes.

YOU WILL NEED
Two wire coat hangers
Wire cutters
White or pink duct tape
Pair of white or pink tights
Fabric glue
Glitter, sequins or
other decorations
Elastic, about 80cm (32in)

2 Place the wings so that the twisted wire necks overlap each other, and tape them together well with the duct tape.

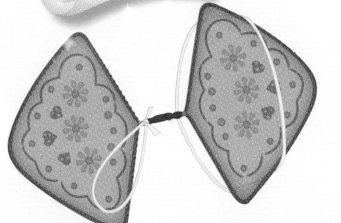

3 Ask an adult to cut the tights down to the knee. Stretch one tight over one of the wings, making sure the toe seam sits on the wire edge. Repeat on the other side and secure the ends in the middle using more duct tape.

Top Tip!

Instead of using tights, you can cover your wire wings with tulle or colored cellophane. Cover each wing before you join them together. Lay the tulle or cellophane on your work surface and apply glue to one side of the wire wing. Lay the wing glue side down on the fabric or cellophane. Repeat to cover the other side. When the glue is completely dry, ask an adult to trim off the excess tulle or cellophane.

4 Decorate your wings. Make patterns with the glue and sprinkle glitter over it; stick on sequins and jewels; you can also glue ribbon around the edges if you wish.

5 For the arm bands, cut the elastic in half and tie the ends of each piece together to make two loops. Hold one end of an elastic loop behind the taped join and put the other end of the loop over the wings and through the elastic. Pull it tight to secure the elastic. Attach the other elastic loop on the other side of the join on the wings. Put your arms through the elastic and flutter away.

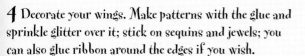

Spell Bells

Tinkerbell wasn't given her name for nothing! Every fairy knows that to help you with your spells and fairy wishes, you need some very special jingle bells.

YOU WILL NEED
2–6 tinsel pipe cleaners
Metallic tape
1–8 jingle bells
Thin ribbon, 30cm (12in)
long, for each jingle bell

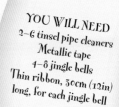

1 How many pipe cleaners you use will depend on their length and how large you want your spell bell frame to be. Aim to make a circle about 10cm (4in) in diameter. If you have long pipe cleaners, just use one and bend it into a circle and twist the ends together. If you need to, join two pipe cleaners together first before bending them into a circle and joining the ends.

2 Twist more pipe cleaners around and around your first circle to make it double the thickness and strength. Tuck in all the ends neatly and tape them down using metallic tape.

3 Thread a jingle bell onto a length of ribbon and tie it onto your frame. Add the other bells in the same way, spacing them evenly but leaving a clear space large enough for you to hold the frame without touching any bells.

4 When you are happy with the spacing of your bells, tie each ribbon in a double knot to secure it and then tie a bow.

Wishing Wand

Every fairy needs a good wand to make her magic. This wand has one plain silver side and one glittery silver side, but you can make both sides the same if you want to.

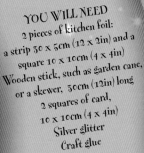

YOU WILL NEED
2 pieces of kitchen foil:
a strip 30 x 5cm (12 x 2in) and a
square 10 x 10cm (4 x 4in)
Wooden stick, such as garden cane,
or a skewer, 30cm (12in) long
2 squares of card,
10 x 10cm (4 x 4in)
Silver glitter
Craft glue

1 Lay the strip of kitchen foil shiny side down on your work surface. Dab a little glue along one long edge. Place your stick straight onto the sticky edge and make sure it is stuck down.

2 Keeping the stick straight and the foil flat, roll up the stick in the foil. Apply glue along the other edge of the foil and stick it down.

3 Draw a star onto both pieces of card and ask an adult to help you cut them out.

4 Place the square of foil shiny side down. Brush one side of one star with glue and stick it in the center of the foil.

5 Cut out the foil-covered star.

6 Apply glue to one side of the other star and cover it with silver glitter.

7 Lay the stars foil and glitter sides down and apply glue to both card sides. Place the end of your stick straight down the center of one star.

8 With the points of the stars aligned, place the other star on top, glue side down, and press the two stars together with the stick in the middle. Leave to dry.

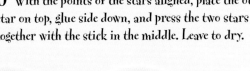

Magic Flowers

Using the same method as for the wand, you can create gorgeous colorful fairy flowers. Cover the sticks with green tissue paper instead of foil and draw a flower shape instead of a star.

1 For each flower, cover a stick with green tissue paper and draw a flower with a circle in the center onto the two pieces of card. Ask an adult to cut out the flowers and then stick them together onto one end of the stick, as before.

2 Tear up the yellow tissue paper into little pieces and scrunch them up. Apply glue to the circle in the center of your flower. Stick the yellow tufts of paper onto it, making sure there are no gaps.

3 Tear up the pink tissue paper and scrunch them as before. Apply glue to the petals and stick the pink tufts of paper in place.

4 Repeat to decorate the other side of the flower. You can use different colored tissue paper if you like because these are magic flowers!

YOU WILL NEED
Wooden stick, such as garden cane or a skewer, 30cm (12in) long
1 strip of green tissue paper, 30 x 5cm (12 x 2in)
2 squares of card, 10 x 10cm (4 x 4in)
Yellow tissue paper
Pink tissue paper
One other color of tissue paper (optional)
Craft glue
Plant pot and floristry foam (optional)

Bluebell Sapphire says:
'Why not make a whole bunch of colorful flowers and give them to a friend or family member? You can put them in a vase, or stick them in a pot using a piece of florist's foam to hold them in place.'

Glamorous Fairies

Fairies always spend time on their appearance, so they look as pretty as can be. You can do the same to complete your fairy outfit.

Flower Fairy Face Paint

YOU WILL NEED
Make-up sponge
Lilac, bright pink and silver
or white face paint
Small clean paintbrush or
make-up brush
Facial glitter
Stick-on body jewels

1 Using a make-up sponge, ask an adult to help you apply lilac face paint all over the eye area, starting with the eyelid and taking the color up above the eyebrow and out in a curve around the outer corner of the eye. Bring the color just below the eye too and blend it outwards so that it fades off at the edges. Put a small dab on your forehead, just above your nose and between your eyes.

2 Using the other end of the make-up sponge, ask an adult to help you apply bright pink face paint over the eyelids, on top of the lilac. Apply the color by pressing it gently on and blending the edges. Add a small dab between the eyes in the middle of the lilac.

3 Using a brush, apply white curls, scrolls and dots of white or silver paint to add detail. Start with a curl from the corner of the eye outwards and upwards, then add little teardrops below this around the outer corner of the eye. Repeat on the other eye, making sure the design is the same on both sides.

4 Stick a body jewel between your eyes and add others as you wish.

5 Using a clean brush, apply pink paint for color on your lips.

Flower Water Perfume

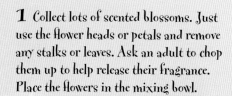

1 Collect lots of scented blossoms. Just use the flower heads or petals and remove any stalks or leaves. Ask an adult to chop them up to help release their fragrance. Place the flowers in the mixing bowl.

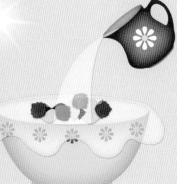

YOU WILL NEED
2 large handfuls of freshly chopped flower blossoms such as rose, lavender, lilac, orange blossom and honeysuckle
Mixing bowl
Piece of cheesecloth or muslin larger than the bowl
500ml / 18 fl. oz / 2 cups of water
Plate

2 Place the fabric over the bowl and fill with your flower blossoms.

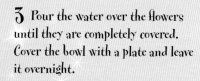

3 Pour the water over the flowers until they are completely covered. Cover the bowl with a plate and leave it overnight.

4 The following day, remove the plate, lift up the edges of the fabric and gently squeeze the water through the cloth and into the bowl.

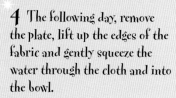

5 Ask an adult to help you pour the liquid into a small pan and simmer on top of the stove until there is about two tablespoons of liquid remaining.

6 Let the liquid cool, then pour it into a small dark bottle where it will keep for about a month.

Chapter 2
Fairy Food

From juicy, plump berries to melt-in-the-mouth cakes, fairies love every kind of sweet treat and dainty delicacy. With a little bit of fairy magic, they can turn the most mundane ingredients into a mouth-watering banquet. All you need are some simple items that you probably have at home already – things like bananas, berries, honey, ice cream, flour, sugar, eggs and butter. Add some pretty colored icing, fairy-shaped cookie cutters and plenty of chocolate drops, mini marshmallows or multi-colored sprinkles, and you have everything you need to create a feast fit for a fairy.

Fantastic Fairy Cakes

As their name suggests, these scrumptious little cakes are fit for any fairy tea party. They're light as air, really tasty and pretty as can be. You can make the icing in your favorite color and decorate the cakes with any topping you like. They're so easy to make, it's like… MAGIC!

Preparation time: 20 minutes
Cooking time: 20 minutes
Makes 12 cakes

YOU WILL NEED

12 pretty paper cake cases
Baking tray or 12-hole muffin tin

For the cakes
110g (4oz) butter (soft)
110g (4oz) caster (superfine) sugar
2 medium eggs
110g (4oz) self-raising flour
½ teaspoon baking powder

For butter-cream icing
110g (4oz) icing (confectioner's) sugar
110g (4oz) butter (soft)
2–3 drops of food coloring

• For vanilla butter cream, add half a teaspoon of vanilla extract
• For orange or lemon butter cream, add up to 1 tablespoon of orange or lemon juice (add it a teaspoon at a time and taste as you go)
• For chocolate butter cream, add up to three tablespoons of cocoa powder (add two first and taste)

For sugar icing
500g (11oz) icing (confectioner's) sugar
2–3 tablespoons water
2–3 drops of food coloring of your choice

To make the cakes

1 Preheat the oven to 180°C/350°F/Gas 4. Put the butter and sugar into a mixing bowl and mix them together well, using a fork to break up the butter.

2 Crack the eggs into another bowl and beat them. Then pour the eggs into the sugar and butter mixture and stir them in well.

3 Sieve the flour and baking powder into the bowl and mix it in with a metal spoon.

Sugar icing

Put the sieved icing sugar in a bowl and add two tablespoons of water and your chosen coloring. Mix it until it is smooth. Add a little more water if you need to, a drop at a time. Spread the icing smoothly over your cakes with a palette knife.

Decorate your cakes

Here's the really fun bit! Add sprinkles, sweets, colored balls... whatever you like!

4 Put the cases on the baking tray or muffin tin. Spoon the mixture into the cake cases, filling them to just over halfway. Ask an adult to put them in the oven for you.

5 After 20 minutes, your cakes should be golden brown and smell delicious. Ask an adult to take them out of the oven and leave them to cool.

Ruby Rose says:
'Leave the door closed while the cakes are cooking. No peeking!'

Butterfly Cakes

Fairies love butterflies, and what better way to flatter fluttery friends than to make special butterfly cakes for them. Ask an adult to cut a circular slice off the top of a fairy cake and cut it in half to form two wings. Fill the hole with your chosen filling and then stick the two 'wings' into it. Then add some decorations between the wings.

Try some of the following fairy-favorite combinations:

Butter-cream icing with sparkly balls
Whipped cream and a couple of fresh raspberries
Raspberry jam and chocolate chips
Chocolate spread and a dusting of icing sugar

Butter-cream icing

Put the butter in a bowl and sieve the icing sugar on top a little at a time, mixing it in as you go, until it's creamy and smooth. Add your chosen flavor or coloring and mix well. Spread the icing smoothly over your cakes with a palette knife. Or ask an adult to help you use a piping bag. Cover the cakes with swirls or peaks of icing.

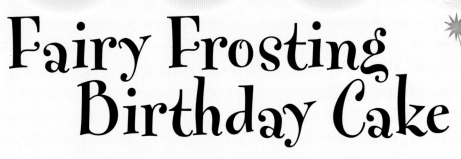

Fairy Frosting Birthday Cake

This delicious cake is a classic Victoria sponge, but you can color it pink, if you wish, for a special fairy touch. Use strawberry icing sugar for the frosting and then decorate your cake with shapes cut out of ready-to-roll icing and sprinkle with edible glitter.

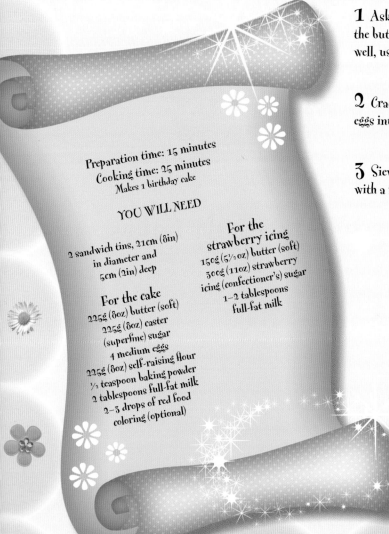

Preparation time: 15 minutes
Cooking time: 25 minutes
Makes 1 birthday cake

YOU WILL NEED

2 sandwich tins, 21cm (8in) in diameter and 5cm (2in) deep

For the cake
225g (8oz) butter (soft)
225g (8oz) caster (superfine) sugar
4 medium eggs
225g (8oz) self-raising flour
½ teaspoon baking powder
2 tablespoons full-fat milk
2–3 drops of red food coloring (optional)

For the strawberry icing
150g (5½oz) butter (soft)
300g (11oz) strawberry icing (confectioner's) sugar
1–2 tablespoons full-fat milk

1 Ask an adult to preheat the oven to 180°C / 350°F / Gas 4. Put the butter and sugar into a mixing bowl and mix them together well, using a fork to break up the butter.

2 Crack the eggs into another bowl and beat them. Then pour the eggs into the sugar and butter mixture and beat them in well.

3 Sieve the flour and baking powder into the bowl and mix it in with a metal spoon. Add the milk and food coloring.

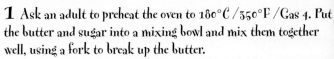

4 Grease the sandwich tins, then pour half the mixture into one and half into the other. Ask an adult to put the cakes in the oven and bake for about 25 minutes.

Bluebell Sapphire says:

'Ask an adult to test the cakes by piercing them in the middle with a fine skewer. If the skewer comes out clean, the cakes are done.'

5 Let them stand in their tins for a couple of minutes, then ask an adult too carefully turn them onto a wire rack to cool.

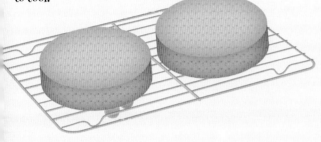

6 To make the icing, beat the butter in a mixing bowl.

7 Sieve half the icing sugar on top and beat until it is creamy and smooth. Add the remaining sugar and one tablespoon of milk and beat again. Add a little more milk if you need to.

8 To ice your cake, put one sponge on your cake plate and spread half the icing on top using a palette knife.

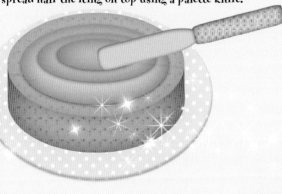

9 Place the other cake on top to make a sandwich. Then spread the rest of the icing over the top.

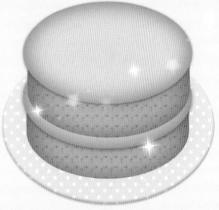

10 Decorate your cake with ready-made edible flowers or cut your own flower, butterfly and fairy shapes out of ready-to-roll icing, using mini cookie cutters.

Top Tip!
If you can't find strawberry icing sugar, you can just use normal icing sugar. Mash up some fresh strawberries and mix them in at the final stage instead of the milk.

Fairy Cookies

Cookie cutters come in many shapes and sizes, including wonderful fairy designs, such as crowns, carriages, unicorns and fairy castles. You can also use flowers, butterflies and stars. Think about all the things that fairies love and you will probably have lots of ideas.

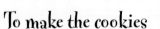

Preparation time: 20 minutes
Cooking time: 12–20 minutes
Makes about 30 cookies

YOU WILL NEED

Selection of
cookie cutters

For the cookies
150g (5½oz) all-purpose
(plain) flour
½ teaspoon
baking powder
Small pinch salt
55g (2oz) butter, diced
55g (2oz) soft
brown sugar
1 medium egg
25g (1oz) golden syrup

For the sugar icing
150g (5½oz) icing
(confectioner's) sugar
1–2 tablespoons of water
1–2 drops pink
food coloring
Colorful edible sprinkles

To make the cookies

1 Ask an adult to preheat the oven to 160°C / 325°F / Gas 3. Sieve the flour, salt and baking powder into a mixing bowl. Add the diced butter and mix it in well using your fingers, then stir in the sugar with the spoon.

2 Add the egg to the golden syrup and mix together with a fork. Add this to the mixture and beat well until the dough comes together.

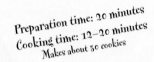

3 Flour the work surface, dough and a rolling pin well, then roll out the dough to about 5mm (¼in) thick.

4 Cut out the cookies using the cookie cutters and place them on a greased baking tray. Clump the left-over dough, roll it out and cut some more shapes.

5 Ask an adult to put your cookies in the oven and keep an eye on them while they're cooking. When they're done, place them on a wire rack to cool.

To make the icing

Put the sieved icing sugar in the mixing bowl and add a tablespoon of water and a drop of coloring. Mix it until it is smooth. Add a little more water if you need to, a drop at a time.

Decorate your cookies

Spread the pink icing onto your cookies and sprinkle with colorful sprinkles.

Daisy Pearl says:

'Don't waste any of the precious dough! Keep rolling it out until you've used it all up to make delicious fairy cookies.'

Toadstool Cookies

Make chocolate cookies, cut them out in the shape of a toadstool and decorate them with red icing and white-chocolate chips. To do this, use 110g (4oz) self-raising flour and 2 tablespoons of cocoa powder. The rest of the cookie ingredients are the same.

You could also make round cookies and cut ready-made red icing into a toadstool shape to decorate them. Then press the chocolate chips into the icing.

37

Special Sweet Delights

Fairies love to eat sweet things such as ice cream and bonbons. But they also like to eat fresh berries plucked from gardens and hedgerows and use them in their special recipes.

YOU WILL NEED
All your favorite berries
Icing (confectioner's) sugar

Berry Delight

1 Pull out the strawberries' stalks. If they are very big, ask an adult to cut them into halves or quarters.

2 Put all the berries into a bowl and mix them together.

3 Sieve a little icing sugar over them. Like magic, the sugar will melt into the juices and make the berries nice and sweet.

4 You can eat these as they are or add a little cream, yoghurt or ice cream. Yummy!

Honey Nectar

YOU WILL NEED
Creamy natural yoghurt
Clear runny honey or maple syrup

1 Pour some creamy natural yoghurt into a glass bowl or cup.

2 Take a teaspoon of honey or maple syrup. Hold it up above the center of your bowl until a thin trail of honey starts to fall onto the yoghurt, then move your spoon slowly and carefully in increasing circles to make a spiral shape.

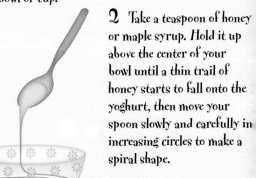

Must-be-Magic Ice-cream Sundae

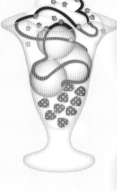

1 Put the chopped strawberries into the bottom of the glass.

2 Use a small ice-cream scoop, if you have one, or a metal spoon, and place little balls or curls of strawberry ice cream onto the fruit.

3 Pour a couple of teaspoons of strawberry sauce or coulis over the top.

4 For a special treat, add a little whipped cream and top with another drizzle of sauce and some chopped nuts or sprinkles.

Peanut Butter Bonbons

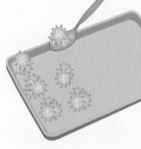

1 Ask an adult to help you melt the peanut butter and butter together in a saucepan until warm and smooth.

2 Mix the icing sugar and cereal in a mixing bowl, pour the peanut-butter mixture over it and then mix carefully with a metal spoon.

3 Roll spoonfuls of the mixture into balls and place them on a large plate or baking tray to cool.

4 Ask an adult to melt the chocolate in a small bowl over a pan of water or in the microwave.

5 Using a toothpick, dip the peanut butter balls into the melted chocolate and place them on waxed paper to set.

Tasty Banana Boat

YOU WILL NEED

1 banana
Vanilla ice cream
or frozen yoghurt
Whipped cream or
thick natural yoghurt
Clear runny honey or
maple syrup
Chopped hazelnuts
1 wafer

1 Ask an adult to cut the banana in half, lengthways. Lay the two halves in a bowl in the shape of a boat.

2 Using a small ice cream scoop or spoon, scoop out some balls of ice cream or frozen yoghurt and place them down the middle of the banana.

3 Add a little whipped cream or yoghurt to fill in the gaps.

4 Drizzle a little runny honey or syrup over the top in a zigzag pattern and then scatter with the chopped hazelnuts.

5 Anchor the wafer in the ice cream at one end to make a sail.

Fruit Smoothie

Makes 2 smoothies

YOU WILL NEED

1 banana
6 strawberries
350ml (12 fl. oz)
chilled milk
1–2 teaspoons
runny honey

1 Ask an adult to slice the banana and strawberries. Put the fruit in the blender.

2 Pour in the milk and add the honey. Put the lid on the blender and blend the ingredients until smooth.

3 Pour the smoothie into glasses and add a couple of straws and a cocktail umbrella to decorate.

Rose-blush Meringues

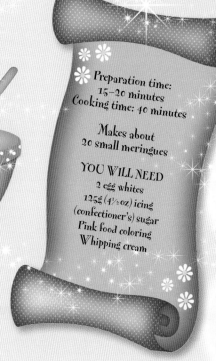

Preparation time:
15–20 minutes
Cooking time: 40 minutes

Makes about
20 small meringues

YOU WILL NEED
2 egg whites
125g (4½oz) icing
(confectioner's) sugar
Pink food coloring
Whipping cream

1 Ask an adult to help you whisk the egg whites until they are stiff and form a peak when you lift out the whisk.

2 Whisk in half the sugar, adding it a little at a time. Add a drop or two of food coloring until the mixture is the shade of pink that you like.

3 Fold in the rest of the sugar using a metal spoon. Ask an adult to preheat the oven to 160°C /325°F /Gas 3.

4 You don't have to pipe your meringues but they will be prettier if you do. You can use a teaspoon to spoon a little mixture onto the baking tray, making circles about 8–10cm (3–4in) in diameter. Otherwise, fill a piping bag and squeeze out the mixture.

Ask an adult to help you put the meringues in the oven. Bake for 40 minutes until they feel firm. Turn off the oven but leave them in there to cool down.

5 Whisk the cream until it forms stiff peaks when you remove the whisk. If you like, you can add a drop of pink food coloring to make the cream pink.

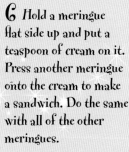

6 Hold a meringue flat side up and put a teaspoon of cream on it. Press another meringue onto the cream to make a sandwich. Do the same with all of the other meringues.

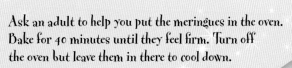

Teatime Bites

No teatime feast is complete without some dainty sandwiches fit for a fairy. Jasmine Emerald's favorite are raspberry jam, but you could also make your sandwiches with peanut butter, honey or chocolate spread.

YOU WILL NEED
Makes 6 sandwiches

6-12 slices of bread
Butter
Jam
Cookie cutters: large circle, small circle, star and heart

1 Using the large circular cookie cutter, cut out six tops and six bottoms for your sandwiches (or as many as you want to make). Try to cut two circles out of each slice of bread.

2 Put half the circles of bread to one side for the sandwich lids. Spread butter and jam onto one side of the remaining circles.

3 Using the small circular cookie cutter, cut a small circle out of the center of two of the lids. Cut two stars and two hearts out of the centers of the remaining lids.

4 Place the lids with the cut-out shapes on your sandwiches, and tuck in.

Fairy Tea Party

The theme has to be pink, pink, pink! Here are some ideas:

Put up your bunting
(see pages 52–53).

Make a plateful of
delicious Teatime Bites
and some Fairy Cakes
and Cookies
(see pages 32 and 36).

Put some flowers on
the table – just a few
single flowers in small
jars will do.

Tie a ribbon bow onto
the back of each chair.

Use the prettiest glasses and cups you can find to set your table.

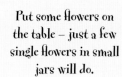

Lay the table with a pretty tablecloth and pink napkins.

Fairy Place Mat

Fairies love meal-times. It's a chance for them all to get together and discuss the day's events. Make your meal-times special with a place mat based on your favorite fairy – you could make one for other members of your family, too.

YOU WILL NEED
A5 colored card
Tracing paper and pencil
White paper
Coloring pens, pencils
or crayons
Scissors
Craft glue
Stickers
Glitter
A5 sheet of
sticky-back plastic

1 Use the above template of Amber Lily to trace your fairy figure onto a piece of white paper. You can trace one of the other fairies in this book if you wish. Then, use your coloring pens, pencils or crayons to decorate your fairy figure.

2 Think about what other things you'd like in your picture – some butterflies, bees, flowers or toadstools, perhaps. Trace as many of these as you wish onto paper and color them in. You may also want to draw a tree or even a fairy cottage.

3 When you've finished, ask an adult to cut out your fairy and all the other shapes. Now you're ready to glue them onto your piece of card.

4 When all your pictures are glued in place, add some stickers or dab spots of glue onto the card and sprinkle them with glitter.

5 Ask an adult to cover your place mat with some clear sticky-back plastic.

Chapter 3
Fairy Grotto

Fairies live among the sweetly scented flowers in the garden, often using a large petal for their bed, with the softest feathers to keep them warm and a large leaf to keep the rain off. Their carpet is springy moss or plush green grass and their furniture is built from twigs, acorns and pinecones. Bring some fairy touches into your bedroom, with flower garlands, fairy lights and homemade bunting. With pretty fabric, colorful paper, sparkly decorations and lots of imagination, you can make all sorts of fairy items to transform your room into a magical fairy grotto.

Fairy Bedroom

Sleep is very important for fairies, as working all that magic uses up a lot of energy. Have fun making your bedroom cosy and fairy-like.

YOU WILL NEED
2 lengths of tulle or netting,
5m (10ft) long and
137cm (54in) wide
2 elastic bands
50cm (20in) matching ribbon
20cm (8in) fine wire
Wire cutters
Hammer
Large picture nail or hook

Magical Bed Canopy

1 Take one end of one piece of tulle and bunch it up in your hand. Wrap an elastic band around it a few times to secure it tightly, positioning it about 10cm (4in) from the end. Do the same with one end of the other piece of tulle.

2 Lay the two gathered ends side by side and tie the length of ribbon around them to hold them together. Wrap the ribbon around the tulle two or three times and then tie a bow at the front.

3 Thread the wire under the ribbon at the back and twist the ends together around the ribbon. Make a small loop about 2.5cm (1in) up by twisting the wires together again. Ask an adult to trim off the ends with wire cutters.

4 Ask an adult to hammer the picture nail or hook into the wall above your bed. Make sure it is centered in the middle of the bed a couple of meters (yards) above it. Hang up the canopy by hooking the wire loop over the nail or hook. Arrange one piece of tulle on each side of the bed and snuggle up under your pretty canopy.

Flower Headboard

Decorate the headboard or frame of your bed with artificial flowers, ribbon roses (see page 9) and pretty bows. If you can't tie them around your headboard, stick them onto it – or onto the wall behind your bed – using sticky tack.

Twinkling Lights

Ask an adult to wind a string of fairy lights around your headboard or bed frame to give your bed a magical look. Pretty flower shapes in white or pink are the best choice for fairies.

Ruby Rose says:
'A good night's sleep refreshes my magical powers. Here are some ideas for transforming your bed into one fit for a fairy.'

49

Sweet Dreams Pillow

1 Ask an adult to iron the fusible web onto the back of your fairy-print fabric. Then cut out your chosen fairy motifs from the fabric.

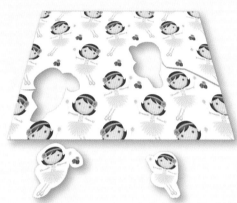

YOU WILL NEED
Iron and paper-backed fusible web
Piece of fabric with fairy motifs
Fabric scissors
Plain pillowcase
Fabric glue
Matching ribbon, long enough to edge the pillowcase

2 Decide where on the pillowcase you would like to position the fairies. Remember you are going to lay your head on the pillow, so it may be best to keep the decorations at the edges and corners. Peel the backing paper off the shapes and ask an adult to iron them in position.

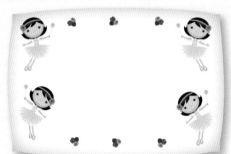

3 Apply glue to the back of the ribbon and carefully stick it in place along the edge of the pillowcase.

Jasmine Emerald says:
'You don't have to use fabric-bonding web. You can just cut out the shapes and stick them in place with fabric glue.'

Templates

Use these templates to create a fairy for your cushion.

Fluffy Cushion

1 Ask an adult to iron the fusible web onto the back of the four fabric pieces.

2 Using tracing paper, trace the outline of the fairy's hair onto the back of the fabric you've chosen. Do the same for all the other elements of the fairy, tracing the face, body, arms and legs onto the same piece of fabric, and the wings and the dress onto different colored pieces.

3 Ask an adult to cut out all the shapes. Peel off the backing paper and position the shapes on the front of your cushion, making sure your fairy is in the middle of the cushion. Ask an adult to iron them in place.

4 Using fabric pens, draw on the fairy's eyes, nose and mouth, copying the template.

5 Make the wand by cutting one piece of ribbon 6cm (2½ in) long for the handle. Cut four pieces 2.5cm (1in) long. Dab a little fabric glue in the middle of the first short piece and stick a second piece centrally on top at right angles to make a cross. Stick on the other two short pieces diagonally to make a star shape. Glue the handle onto the cushion, with one end in your fairy's hand. Glue the star shape on top of the wand.

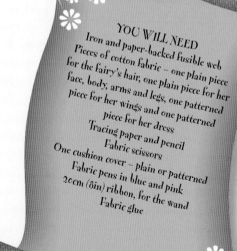

YOU WILL NEED
Iron and paper-backed fusible web
Pieces of cotton fabric – one plain piece for the fairy's hair, one plain piece for her face, body, arms and legs, one patterned piece for her wings and one patterned piece for her dress
Tracing paper and pencil
Fabric scissors
One cushion cover – plain or patterned
Fabric pens in blue and pink
20cm (8in) ribbon, for the wand
Fabric glue

Fabric Bunting

Bunting is so pretty and it's a great way to use up lots of scraps of cotton fabric or old dresses and skirts that you've grown out of.

1 To make a template for the bunting, draw a triangle on the card. Ask an adult to help you cut out the triangle to make your template.

2 Work out how long you want your bunting to be and cut the fabric tape to length, leaving about 30cm (12in) extra at each end for the ties.

3 Using the template and pinking shears, ask an adult to cut out as many fabric triangles as you need.

4 Apply fabric glue to the top edge of your first triangle. Measure 30cm (12in) in from one end of the tape for the tie, and stick the triangle in place. Leave a gap of about 5.5cm (2¼in) and stick the next triangle in place. Continue to the end, alternating the fabrics and colors.

5 Cut lengths of ribbon, about 24cm (9½in) long, and tie them in between your fabric triangles.

YOU WILL NEED
A4 piece of card
Pencil and scissors
White or pink fabric tape,
1cm (½in) wide
Pinking shears
Fabric scraps in fairy colors
and patterns, each at least
15 x 15cm (6 x 6in)
Fabric glue
Tulle ribbon

Ruby Rose says:
'Tie your bunting between your bedposts, drape it over a mirror, or tie it between two trees in the garden and watch it flutter in the breeze.'

Paper Bunting

You can make decorative bunting out of paper by tracing your favorite fairy characters onto pieces of paper and coloring them in. Then stick your paper fairies onto a piece of string and hang them on the wall.

YOU WILL NEED
Tracing paper and pencil
White paper
Scissors
Coloring pencils, pens or crayons
Stick-on jewels
Piece of string, 1m (3ft 3in) long
Craft glue

Templates

Use these templates to create your fairy bunting figures.

1 Trace each fairy onto the piece of paper. Remember to include the tab, 1cm (½in) wide and 2.5cm (1in) long, coming out of the top of each fairy's head.

2 Color in your fairies and ask an adult to help you cut them out. Add a few sparkly jewels to their hair or dresses.

3 Measure 25cm (10in) in from one end of the string for the tie. Apply glue to the back of the paper tab on your first fairy and wrap it over the string. Leave a gap of about 8cm (3in) and stick on the next fairy. When all the fairies are stuck in place, you can hang up your fairy bunting in your room.

YOU WILL NEED
Tracing paper and pencil
Piece of card, 20 x 20cm (8 x 8in)
Square of contrast fabric,
10 x 10cm (4 x 4in)
Fabric scissors
Pinking shears
Piece of fabric for your flag base,
at least 13 x 20cm (5 x 8in)
Fabric glue
Fabric glitter glue or paint
Wooden stick, such as a garden cane
or skewer, at least 30cm (12in) long

Fancy Flag

Fairies are very patriotic creatures. They're very proud of Fairyland and fly their flags from the top of their castles and carriages. Have fun making one for your bedroom. You can make it out of paper or fabric, but fabric will last longer.

1 Trace the shield shape onto one part of the piece of card and the flower shape onto another part. Enlarge both templates and ask an adult to cut them out.

2 Ask an adult to cut the shield shape out of the contrast fabric with fabric scissors. Using the pinking shears, cut around the edges of the flag fabric to make a decorative edge that will fray less easily.

3 Apply glue to the back of the shield. Measure 4cm (1¾ in) from the right-hand edge of your flag and stick the shield in place.

4 Hold the flower template in the center of the shield and then carefully draw around the edge of it with a pencil or pen. Lift off the template and fill in the flower shape with glitter glue or paint.

5 Draw around the edge of the shield with the fabric glitter glue or paint, too, and decorate the rest of the flag if you wish. Leave the glitter glue to dry.

6 When the glitter glue is dry, apply fabric glue along the back of the left-hand edge of the flag and stick it around the wooden stick.

Glitzy Banner

Make a large paper banner for your bedroom wall and paint on a magical picture, including all the things you can think of that you'd find in fairyland – toadstools, goblins, a fairy castle, butterflies, ladybirds, flowers, stars and, of course, fairies. Copy some of the ideas below and use them in your picture, too.

Bluebell Sapphire's Top Ten Ideas:

1 Write the word 'Fairyland' in your best handwriting along the top of your banner and go over it with paint or felt-tips.

2 Collect some flower petals from the garden and use them to spell out the word 'Fairyland'.

3 Trace the word 'Fairyland' in sparkly glitter pen.

4 Look for the letters that spell the word in an old magazine or newspaper, cut them out and stick them on. Choose letters from headlines in different colors and shapes.

5 Paint patterns on your picture with craft glue and sprinkle them with colorful glitter.

6 Add some sparkly stickers and glitzy stick-on jewels to decorate your fairy banner.

7 Use feathers for fairy wings.

8 Instead of drawing or painting all the shapes above, trace some onto colored paper, cut them out and stick them on.

9 Use little pieces of scrunched-up tissue paper to make flowers or to decorate your butterfly wings.

10 Collect flowers and leaves from the garden and shells from the beach and stick them onto your picture.

Dazzling Jewellery Box

Fairies need somewhere to keep all of their sparkly trinkets. Daisy Pearl has a pretty box embellished with precious gems, covered in lilac satin and lined in purple. You can either buy a little gift box and decorate it, or make your own.

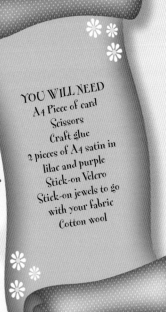

YOU WILL NEED
A4 Piece of card
Scissors
Craft glue
2 pieces of A4 satin in lilac and purple
Stick-on Velcro
Stick-on jewels to go with your fabric
Cotton wool

1 Draw the box outline onto the card, copying the diagram and making the squares 8 x 8cm (3 x 3in), the flaps 1cm (½ in) and the lid fastening 3cm (1¼ in). Ask an adult to cut it out.

2 Glue the card onto the wrong side of the lilac satin and ask an adult to cut it out. Then glue the other side of the card onto the wrong side of the purple satin and cut it out.

3 With your box lining side up, fold up the sides starting with squares 1 and 2. Apply glue to the outside of the flap on 1 and stick it onto the inside of 2. Fold up 3. Apply glue to the outside of the flap and stick it to the inside of 1. Fold up 4. Apply glue to the outside of the flap and stick it to 3. Apply glue to the outside of the flap on 2 and stick it to 4.

4 Cut a piece of Velcro and stick one side onto the top of the outside of 1 and one side onto the inside of the lid flap.

5 Decorate your box with the pretty stick-on jewels.

6 Put some cotton wool in the bottom of the box and tuck some of the left-over satin around it to make a padded base.

Flap
Lid
4
3 | Base | 2
1

Paper Lantern

Make a pretty paper lantern to hang up in your room. You could make lots of lanterns in different colors and hang them up on a string.

1 Fold a piece of paper in half lengthways to make a rectangle. Press the crease firmly to make the fold sharp.

2 Draw a very light pencil line, 2.5cm (1in) in from the long cut edges. Make a series of cuts along the folded edge up to this line, spacing each cut 1cm (½in) apart. Then carefully rub out the pencil line.

3 Unfold the paper and apply glue along the wrong side of one short edge and stick it to the other short edge to make a cylinder.

YOU WILL NEED
A4 colored or
patterned paper
Pencil, ruler and eraser
Scissors
Craft glue
Glitter or glitter glue

4 Cut a strip of paper, approximately 20cm (8in) long and 1.5cm (¾in) wide, and glue it centrally across the top opening of the lantern to make a handle.

5 Decorate your lantern with glitter or glitter glue. Put it around the top and bottom edges and in patterns on the side of the lantern.

Sparkly Door Hanger

Make a special nameplate to hang on your bedroom door.

1 Roll out your clay on a wipe-clean surface with the rolling pin.

2 Ask an adult to use a blunt knife to cut out a rectangle, measuring 8 x 18cm (3 x 7in), from the clay and smooth the edges with your fingers, rounding off the corners.

3 Make a hole in both top corners using the skewer. The holes need to be big enough for you to thread the ribbon through.

4 Neatly write your name on the front of the rectangle using the skewer to score out the letters in the clay. Practise writing your name on a piece of paper the same size first to make sure your letters fit. Leave the clay to dry according to the instructions.

5 Apply glue to the indent of each letter, sprinkle with glitter and gently tap off the excess. You can use the same color glitter for each letter or make each one a different color.

6 Stick gemstones around your name for extra decoration. You can arrange them in the shape of flowers or put them around the edge to make a frame.

7 Thread the ribbon through the holes from front to back and tie the ends together.

YOU WILL NEED
Air-dry clay
Rolling pin
Wooden skewer
Craft glue
Glitter
Gemstones
45cm (18in) thin ribbon

58

Magic Dreamcatcher

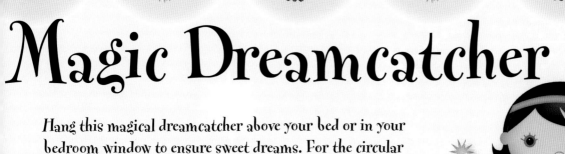

Hang this magical dreamcatcher above your bed or in your bedroom window to ensure sweet dreams. For the circular frame, you need a metal or plastic hoop. You can either buy one or fashion one out of metal wire.

YOU WILL NEED
Metal or plastic hoop,
10cm (4in) in diameter
Ribbon or silver foil
to cover the hoop
Craft glue
Colored embroidery threads
in as many colors as you like
3–5 feathers
Scissors
4–6 large beads or buttons

1 Cover the hoop with ribbon or strips of silver foil and hold the ends in place with glue.

2 Tie embroidery thread to the hoop and wind it around the opposite side, then take it diagonally from side to side around the hoop, winding it around each time. When you want to change colors, knot the thread tightly to the hoop. Tie on a new color and continue weaving from side to side around the hoop, like a spider's web.

3 Tuck the feathers between the threads to hold them in place.

4 Cut a piece of thread, 8cm (3in) long, for each button or bead and knot one end. Thread on the bead or button and tie the other end of the thread to the bottom of the hoop.

5 Cut another 8cm (3in) length of thread. Loop it around the top of the hoop and knot the ends together.

Notice Board

Make a notice board for your fairy grotto, where you can keep your cards, pictures and party invitations.

1 Apply glue to one side of the board and stick the wadding on top.

2 Making sure your fabric is wrinkle-free, lay it pattern side down and place the board, wadding side down, on top with an even overlap of fabric all round.

3 Ask an adult for some help. Starting at the center of the bottom edge, apply a dab of glue to the fabric overlap and stick it to the back of the board. Secure using the staple gun. Do the same on the opposite side of the board. Keep working outwards from the center, alternating sides to keep the tension even.

4 When all four sides are secure, trim off the excess fabric at the corners, fold them neatly and staple them in place.

5 Measure 12cm (4¾in) along the top edge from the left corner and mark with a pencil. Measure and mark two more points 12cm (4¾in) apart. Repeat along the bottom edge.

YOU WILL NEED
Craft glue
Wooden board,
35 x 50cm (14 x 20in)
Piece of 70g (20oz) wadding,
35 x 50cm (14 x 20in)
Printed fabric, 51 x 66cm
(20 x 26in)
Staple gun
3.2m (11ft) elastic,
1cm (½in) wide
50cm (20in) ribbon,
1cm (½in) wide

6 Cut eight pieces of elastic, 40cm (16in) long. Staple one end of the first piece to the back of the board in the top-left corner. Take the elastic diagonally over the front of the board and staple the other end to the back of the board at the first mark on the bottom edge. Staple the rest of the pieces parallel to the first, taking them from the first mark on the top edge to the second on the bottom edge. Continue in this way, and then work back in the other direction to crisscross the elastic lengths.

7 Staple one end of the ribbon in each corner on the back of the board to hang it.

Pyjama Case

This pretty fairy-print case will hold your nightie
or pyjamas and look lovely on your bed.

1 Apply glue to the wrong side of one short edge
of the fabric and fold over a 1cm (½in) hem. Fold
over and glue another 1cm (½in) to make a double
hem. Then do the same at the other end of the fabric.

YOU WILL NEED
Fabric glue
Fairy-print fabric,
70 x 35cm (28 x 14in)
70cm (28in) matching
bobble trim
Scissors
1m (3ft 3in) matching ribbon

2 Making sure that your fabric is free
of wrinkles, lay it right side down on your
work surface with the hemmed edges on the
left and right. Fold the short ends into the
center to make a square.

3 Apply glue to the wrong side of the
bottom edges and stick them together. Then
fold the bottom edge 1cm (½in) up and glue
it in place. Repeat along the top edge.

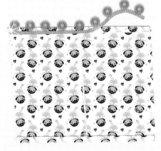

4 Cut the bobble trim in half.
Glue one piece onto the bottom
seam and one piece onto the top
seam to cover the joins, with
the bobbles facing out. Turn
the ends under neatly and glue
them down.

5 Cut four lengths of ribbon
and glue them securely to the
inside of the hemmed opening.
Position each pair about 11cm
(4¼in) from the top and
bottom edges. Tie them in
bows to close your nightie case.

61

Pretty Picture Frame

Make a pretty frame for a fairy picture that you've drawn or for a photograph of your friends or family.

1 Draw a template for your picture frame on graph paper to ensure you cut a perfect square or rectangle. Measure the picture you want to frame and make the inner edge of your frame 5mm (¼in) smaller all round; draw it at least 3cm (1¼in) from the edges of your graph paper. Then draw the outer edge of your frame 3cm (1¼in) outside the first. If you wish, give the top of your frame a scalloped shape. Ask an adult to cut out the picture frame template.

2 Use the graph-paper template together with a long ruler and pencil to draw the frame outline onto a piece of card. Cut out the card frame. Draw a square or rectangle the same size as the outer edge of the frame on some card and cut it out. This will be the back of the picture frame.

3 Apply glue to one side of the card frame and stick it onto the wrong side of a piece of foil paper. Ask an adult to cut away the excess paper, leaving a little overlap to cover the inner and outer edges of the frame. Stick the edges down neatly.

4 Apply glue to the wrong side of the frame, just around the outer edges of the sides and top. Leave the bottom unglued so you can slot your picture into the frame. Stick the back of the frame in place.

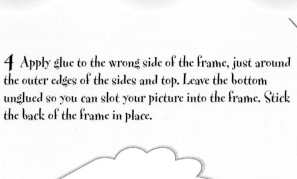

5 So the frame can stand up, draw a triangle onto a piece of card. Fold a flap along the long vertical edge and stick that onto the back of the picture frame, positioning it centrally with the bottom flush with the bottom of the frame.

6 Decorate the front of your frame by gluing on strips of lace trim, cutting the ends into neat diagonals where two pieces meet. Add stick-on gems for extra decoration. Slot your picture into the frame through the gap in the bottom edge, positioning it centrally so that the edges are held in place between the frame and the backing.

Fairy Lavender Bag

These lovely lavender bags will keep your clothes smelling sweet. They also make great presents for members of your family and friends.

YOU WILL NEED
Fine cotton fabric
Saucer
Pinking shears
Dried lavender
30cm (12in) matching ribbon
Polystyrene ball, approximately 2.5cm (1in)
Fabric glue
Black and pink felt-tip pens
Yellow or brown wool or embroidery thread
2 white feathers

1 Lay your fabric right side down. Place the saucer on top and draw around it. Ask an adult to cut out the circle with the pinking shears.

2 Put a handful of dried lavender in the center of the circle and gather up the edges to make a pouch.

3 Wind the ribbon around the neck of the pouch two or three times very tightly and tie it in a secure double knot at the back. Knot the ends of the ribbon together to make a loop to hang your fairy and tie the ends in a bow.

4 Open out the fabric at the neck of the pouch and glue the polystyrene fairy 'head' in the center. Draw her eyes, nose and mouth on the front of the ball (the ribbon should be at the back).

5 Cut equal lengths of wool or embroidery thread to make hair and glue them onto your fairy's head.

6 Glue the ends of the feather wings onto your fairy's back.

Tooth Fairy Bag

However much you love a wobbly tooth, the Tooth Fairy loves it even more! When it falls out, put it in this special bag and leave it by your bed. The Tooth Fairy will whisk it away while you're asleep and, if you've been good, she might leave you a treat.

YOU WILL NEED
Fabric glue
Circle of pretty cotton or satin fabric, approximately 18cm (7in) in diameter
Circular lace doily or circle of netting or tulle, approximately 23cm (9in) in diameter
Hole-puncher
Scissors
1m (3ft 3in) thin ribbon

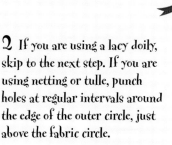

1 Apply glue around the edge of your cotton fabric on the right side. Stick the doily or circle of tulle or netting centrally on top.

2 If you are using a lacy doily, skip to the next step. If you are using netting or tulle, punch holes at regular intervals around the edge of the outer circle, just above the fabric circle.

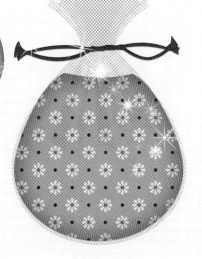

3 Cut the ribbon in half. Thread one piece of ribbon in and out of the holes in the lace, tulle or netting, gathering up the fabric as you go. When you reach your starting point, knot the ends together. Starting on the opposite side, thread the other ribbon through the holes in the same way and knot the ends. Pull the ribbon loops against each other to close your drawstring bag.

Chapter 4
Fairy Fun

There's no end of fun to be had if you're a fairy. When they're not busy granting wishes and performing their fairy duties, they're bound to be out looking for treasure, or just dancing with the butterflies among the flowers. Here are some great ideas for making all sorts of fairy things, from a treasure chest to keep your own treasure, to a ribbon streamer and maracas. Get crafty and make a fairy cottage or carriage out of papier-mâché, transform a cardboard box into a fairy castle, or make a flower fairy collage using petals from the garden.

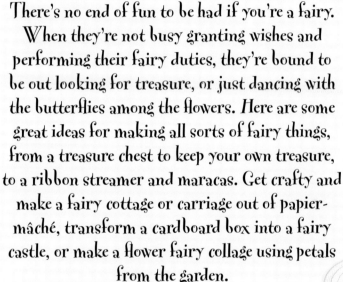

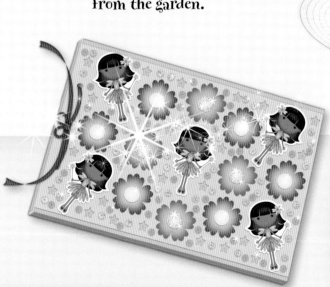

Greeting Cards

Use some of the templates that are shown in this book to make up your own designs for lovely greetings cards.

1 Fold the card in half and press along the crease with your thumb to make it sharp.

2 Choose the templates for your cards. Use either the fairy template shown here or the flower, bee, butterfly or toadstool templates on page 45. Trace the templates onto the card and color them in. Or trace them onto some paper first and cut them out before coloring them in and sticking them to the cards. Then have lots of fun decorating your cards.

Template

Enlarge this fairy template to fit your piece of card

Here are some fairy ideas for decorating your card:

1 Use feathers, lace or paper doily for the fairy wings.

2 Cover the fairy's dress with flower petals or decorate it with sequins, confetti and stick-on gems.

3 Cut the fairy's dress out of brightly colored or foil paper and then cover it with lace or paper doily so the color shows through.

4 Cut a wand out of foil paper and stick it on or stencil the wand onto the card and paint it with glitter glue.

5 Cut the toadstools out of colored foil paper and use little balls of white cotton wool for the spots.

Photograph Fairy

Ask an adult to take a full-length photograph of you wearing a T-shirt and leggings, and then cut a slit across your waist. Carefully push one end of a piece of tulle, measuring 10 x 10cm (4 x 4in), through the slit from front to back to make a skirt for you in the picture. Use some craft glue to stick the end of the tulle to the back of the photograph. Glue a piece of colored card (which is the same size as the photograph) onto the back to cover it. Glue two feathers on either side of your shoulders to make wings. Use a glitter pen to draw yourself a wand on the card and leave it to dry.

Fun Fairy Party

Fairies love parties where they can dance, sing and play music. This colorful ribbon streamer and these fairy maracas are just what you need to give yourself that extra fairy feeling when you're spinning and whirling around.

Fairy Streamers

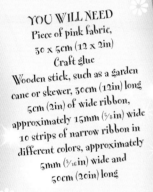

1 Lay the fabric wrong side up on your work surface and apply glue along one long edge. Place your stick straight onto the sticky edge and make sure it is stuck down.

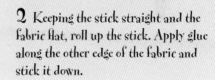

2 Keeping the stick straight and the fabric flat, roll up the stick. Apply glue along the other edge of the fabric and stick it down.

3 Take the short piece of wide ribbon and apply glue to one side. Stick the ends of the narrow ribbon at right angles along the piece of wide ribbon. Alternate the colors.

4 Apply glue onto the stuck-down ends of the narrow ribbon. Place one end of the fabric-covered stick at one end of the row of ribbons and roll it up.

Fairy Maracas

Apply craft glue to the base of a small plastic bottle and stick it onto the wrong side of some colored or foil paper. Ask an adult to cut a circle about 1cm (⅓in) bigger than the base of the bottle. Stick the edges down. Cover the side of the bottle in paper, folding in the edges neatly. Scrunch the paper around the bottle's neck and hold it in place with sparkly tape. Stick on confetti or sequins in different colors and shapes to decorate. Using a funnel, pour some rice into the bottle. Close the lid tightly and tie the three ribbons around it, leaving the ends to dangle down. Get ready to dance your fairy dance!

Fairy Scrapbook

Make up your own scrapbook and use it to store your fairy pictures, drawings, and press flowers and leaves. You can decorate the cover and the pages inside with scraps of ribbon, lace, bobble trim, sequins, sparkly confetti and pretty buttons.

YOU WILL NEED
Hole-puncher
About 20 sheets of white A4 paper
2 pieces of A4-size card for the scrapbook cover
1m (3ft 3in) thin ribbon
Scissors
Fairy wrapping paper, or other fairy pictures
Tracing paper and pencil
Selection of colored paper
Craft glue
Selection of trims, sequins, confetti and buttons

1 Punch three evenly spaced holes using the hole-puncher along one short edge of the paper, about 1cm (⅓in) in from the edge. You may need to punch the paper in batches, a few sheets at a time. Punch corresponding holes in one end of each piece of card, making sure that all the holes line up with each other.

2 Place one piece of card on top of the pile of paper and one on the bottom. Align all the holes, weave the ribbon in and out of the holes and then tie the ends together in a bow.

3 Cut out lots of pictures of fairies from the wrapping paper and stick them onto the card cover.

4 Trace the flower template on page 45 onto different colored pieces of paper, cut out the flowers and stick them on the cover. Cut the same number of flower centers in contrasting colored paper and stick them on the center of each flower.

5 Decorate the cover with confetti, sequins and pretty buttons. If you wish, glue lengths of trim around the edges.

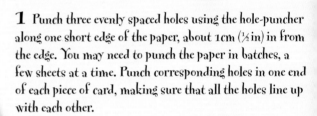

Glitzy Bookmark

All fairies love to read books. This bookmark would also make a lovely present for the girls in your family who love to read.

YOU WILL NEED
Tracing paper and pencil
Paper doily
Scissors
Craft glue
Strip of colored card,
5 x 15cm (2 x 6in)
Glitter pen
Hole-puncher
15cm (6in) ribbon

1 Trace the outline of the fairy shown below onto the paper doily and ask an adult to cut her out.

2 Glue the paper fairy onto the center of the strip of card.

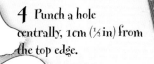

3 Decorate the bookmark using the glitter pen – you could draw a patterned border around the edge of the bookmark and add flowers, butterflies or stars around the fairy. Draw your design lightly in pencil first, and then go over it using the glitter pen.

4 Punch a hole centrally, 1cm (½ in) from the top edge.

5 Fold the ribbon in half and thread the folded end through the hole. Thread the ends of the ribbon through the loop, then pull tight to secure.

Photo Album

Decorate the cover of a photo album to make it special. Cover it with pink, blue, purple, green or orange silky dress-lining fabric, making sure it is wrinkle-free when you glue it on. Fold the edges under neatly on the inside cover and glue them in place. Decorate the cover with pieces of lace and fabric flowers, cut from floral fabric. Add some sparkle with stick-on jewels, pretty buttons, or sequins.

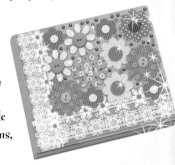

Template

Use this template to create the fairy figure on your bookmark.

Magical Fairy Castle

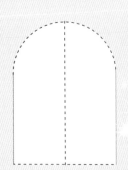

Have fun building your very own Magical Fairy Castle. Store toys, keepsakes and secret things!

1 Cut the flaps off the cardboard box and put them to one side. Turn the box upside down so that its base makes a flat roof. Cover all four sides and the 'roof' with blue foil paper using glue to stick it down. Try to stick the edges down as neatly as you can.

Templates

Enlarge these templates for the castle door and windows to a suitable size to fit your cardboard box.

2 Copying the templates and using a pencil and a ruler for the straight lines, draw the door on the center of one side. Next, draw on some windows. Ask an adult to help cut out your doors and windows, cutting along the dotted lines so that they can be opened by bending them back along the 'hinged' sides.

3 Cover the inside and outside of the windows with silver foil, gluing it in place. Cover the inside and outside of the door with strips of sparkly blue tape.

Template

Use this template to make the castle crenulations.

4 For the castle crenulations, take the box flaps and cut four strips of card 8cm (3in) wide. Stick blue foil paper on both sides of each strip. Copying the template shown above, measure and mark out the crenulations along one edge of each strip. Ask an adult to help cut them out. Then, glue the strips around the top of your castle, so that the crenulations stick up above the flat 'roof'.

5 For the turrets, draw four circles on the wrong side of the blue foil; use a plate about 27cm (10½ in) in diameter to draw around. Ask an adult to help cut out the circles, then fold each one in half and half again. Unfold and cut out one quarter of the circle, cutting along the fold lines. Roll the remains of each circle into a cone shape and glue the edges together.

6 Make little snips around the base of each cone and fan the pieces outwards. Apply glue to the inside of the cut flaps and stick one cone in each corner of the roof.

7 Cut 20 lengths of ribbon, about 15cm (6in) long, and stick five onto the top of each cone using the sparkly tape.

8 Make a miniature fairyland flag, like the one on page 54. Stick the paper flag onto a cocktail stick and pierce the other end into the roof of your castle at the front.

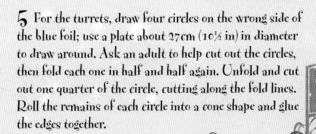

Cosy Fairy Cottage

This cute fairy cottage requires patience to make, as you will need to leave the papier-mâché to dry for a couple of days before you can decorate it.

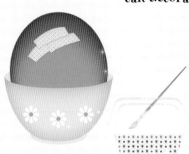

1 Ask an adult to help you blow up the balloon. Dilute some craft glue in an old plastic container: two parts glue to one part water. Protect your work surface well and place the balloon, knot downwards, in a plastic bowl or bucket while you work.

2 Tear the newspaper into pieces, measuring approximately 8 x 5cm (3 x 2in). Dip a strip into the glue mixture, let it absorb the mixture, and then lay it on the balloon, smoothing out any wrinkles with your fingers or the paintbrush. Add another piece in the same way, overlapping the edges.

3 Continue covering the balloon with newspaper strips until the top and sides of the balloon are covered in a layer of paper. Leave the bit where the knot is uncovered and make the bottom edge of the paper as straight and even as possible to create an even base for your cottage.

4 Repeat and cover the balloon with two more even layers. Then leave it to dry thoroughly. You may need to leave it for two to three days. When the balloon has popped, you can peel it away, leaving a dome shape.

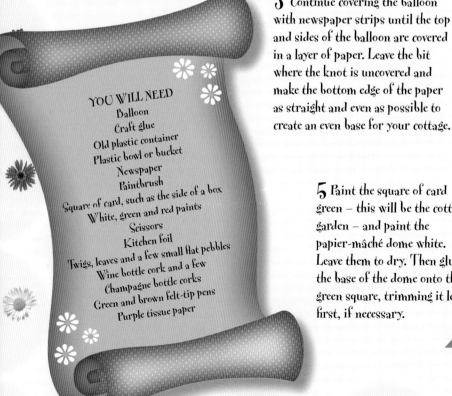

YOU WILL NEED
Balloon
Craft glue
Old plastic container
Plastic bowl or bucket
Newspaper
Paintbrush
Square of card, such as the side of a box
White, green and red paints
Scissors
Kitchen foil
Twigs, leaves and a few small flat pebbles
Wine bottle cork and a few
Champagne bottle corks
Green and brown felt-tip pens
Purple tissue paper

5 Paint the square of card green – this will be the cottage garden – and paint the papier-mâché dome white. Leave them to dry. Then glue the base of the dome onto the green square, trimming it level first, if necessary.

6 Cut two rectangles of kitchen foil to make windows and stick them onto the front of your cottage. Glue four little twigs around the edges of the foil for window frames.

7 For the front door, use three twigs to make the door frame, then fill in the bit between with vertical twigs, stuck side by side.

8 Cover the roof with leaves, overlapping them as you glue them on. Glue the wine bottle cork onto the roof to make a chimney.

9 Draw a vine up one side and across the top of the front door, using the brown pen for the stem and the green pen for leaves. Scrunch up little pieces of purple tissue paper and glue them onto the vine.

10 Paint the Champagne corks red with white spots to make toadstools and glue them onto the green card. Glue the pebbles like stepping stones from the front door through the garden.

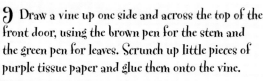

Glittering Fairy Carriage

Make another papier-mâché dome and paint it with gold paint and glitter to make a sparkly, luxurious fairy carriage. Draw around a glass onto a piece of card to make four wheels; cut them out and paint them gold with black spokes and tires, then glue two onto each side of the carriage. Use purple or red foil sweet wrappers for the carriage windows and two wooden skewers painted gold for the harness.

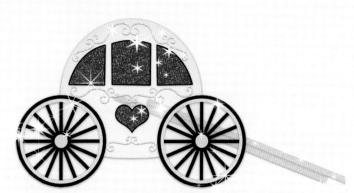

Fairyland Map

Fairyland is a secret, magical place, full of fantastic creatures, beautiful countryside, rivers and lakes and flowers and butterflies in every color you can think of. Imagine what it's like and then draw a map, marking on all the main landmarks.

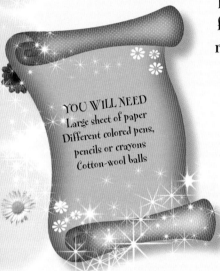

YOU WILL NEED
Large sheet of paper
Different colored pens, pencils or crayons
Cotton-wool balls

Here are some hints from Ruby Rose to get you started:

1 Fairyland itself is like a magical island in the sky. On a large sheet of paper, draw the outline of the island, then surround it with blue sky and fluffy white clouds made from balls of cotton wool.

2 Draw a sun and a multi-colored rainbow above the island.

3 Mark on your map the Mysterious Meadow, which grows all kinds of colorful flowers, the Enchanted Wood and the Magical Toadstool Circle.

4 Draw the river leading to the Wishing Lake.

5 Decide where the Fairy Castle would be and draw it on.

6 Add all of the fairies' cottages, the Unicorn Paddock and Goblin Glade, where the goblins live.

7 Draw lots of paths leading to all the different places, so that the fairies can find their way around.

Woodland Fairy Friends

Butterflies and ladybirds are very good friends of the fairies. Whenever you see a butterfly or ladybird, keep your eyes open because there could be a fairy nearby!

YOU WILL NEED
Tracing paper and pencil
Sheet of green paper
Felt in red, orange, bright pink, black, yellow, purple and pale pink
Scissors
Craft glue
Black felt-tip pen

1 Trace the outline of the ladybird and two butterflies, using the templates shown on the left, onto the green paper.

2 Trace one butterfly's wings onto orange felt and the other onto bright pink felt. Ask an adult to help cut out the shapes and then stick them in position on the paper.

3 Trace the heads and bodies of the ladybird and two butterflies onto black felt. Cut them out and stick them on.

4 Trace the ladybird's wings onto red felt. Cut them out and stick them on the body.

5 Trace the spots onto black felt, cut them out and stick them on the ladybird's wings.

6 Trace the first butterfly's wing details onto the purple and pale pink felt. Cut them out and stick them on. Do the same for the second butterfly, using the yellow and red felt.

7 Using the felt-tip pen, draw the antennae and the ladybird's legs.

Templates

Enlarge these butterfly and ladybird templates to fit your piece of paper.

Garden Weathervane

Fairies are very in tune with nature and can often sense what the weather's going to be like or what time it is without even checking their weathervane or sundial.

YOU WILL NEED
Tracing paper and pencil
Colored card
Scissors
Glitter pen
Glitter tape
Straw
Drawing pin
Pencil with eraser
on the end

1 Trace the arrowhead and tail onto the card, using the templates shown below, and ask an adult to help cut them out. Decorate the arrow tip with the glitter pen and draw a fairy on the tail.

2 Tape the arrowhead onto one end of the straw and the tail onto the other end.

3 Ask an adult to push the drawing pin through the center of the straw and into the eraser on the end of the pencil. Make sure the straw can turn easily.

Templates

Enlarge these templates for the arrowhead and tail so that they will fit nicely on the end of your straw.

4 Find a good spot in the garden and push t end of the pencil into the earth. Watch as the wind turns your weathervane round.

Special Sundial

A sundial enables you to tell the time according to the sun's position in the sky and the shadow that is cast onto its face by the gnomon, which must point due North.

1 Draw a circle on the card by drawing around a plate or bowl which is about 20cm (8in) in diameter. Ask an adult to cut out the circle and then draw a straight line from its center point to the edge.

2 Fold the square of colored paper diagonally in half to make a triangle. Snip 5mm (¼in) into the fold and turn both edges up by this amount to create a flat base.

3 Glue the sides of the triangle together. Apply glue to the flat base of the triangle and stick it onto the line on the face of the sundial, with the straight edge of the triangle at the edge of the circle and the tapered point in the center.

4 Take your sundial outside with your compass and position it so that the straight edge is pointing due North. Every hour, go and check the position of the shadow on the face of your sundial and mark the time on its face where the shadow falls.

YOU WILL NEED
Black felt-tip pen
Card, at least
25 x 25cm (10 x 10in),
for the sundial face
20cm (8in) plate or bowl
Scissors
Colored paper
for the gnomon,
10 x 10cm (4 x 4in)
Craft glue
Compass

N →

Pretty Gift Bags

Fairies love to give their friends little gifts and presents.
These little gift bags work perfectly for small presents,
sweets or party favors.

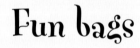

1 For each bag, use a piece of colored paper
measuring 29 x15cm/ 11½ x 6in. Fold in both
long edges by 1cm (½ in) and stick them down.
Fold in both short edges by 1.5cm (¾ in) and
stick them down.

2 Fold the paper in half
with wrong sides together,
making sure the two short
sides meet exactly. Glue both
sides of the bag together.

3 Dip one of the fairy cookie
cutters in one of the paints and
press it onto the paper. Use a
different shape for each color, or
wash and dry the cookie cutter
before changing colors. Decorate the
front of your bag and leave it to dry
before turning it over and decorating
the back in the same way.

4 Punch two holes in the
center of the top edge of
the bag.

Fun bags

If you don't want to make your own
bag, use plain paper sandwich bags
and decorate them using some heart
shapes cut out of old fabric scraps.
Fold both top edges over together and
punch holes through both layers, then
thread a pretty ribbon through and
fasten with a bow.

5 Cut the cord or ribbon
in half and thread one piece
through the holes on each
side of the bag. Knot both
ends on the inside of the bag.

Secrets Box

Découpage is a great way to decorate a plain surface with cut-out pictures. All you need is a box with a lid, such as a gift box or shoebox, and lots of fairy pictures cut out from wrapping paper, old books, magazines or calendars.

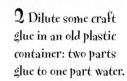

1 Cut out all the letters and pictures you want to use to cover your box and have a play around to see where you want to place them.

2 Dilute some craft glue in an old plastic container: two parts glue to one part water.

3 Using your paintbrush, paint the back of the first picture with the glue solution and stick it in place on the box. Build up your design, overlapping pictures if you wish. Smooth out any wrinkles or air bubbles with your fingers or the paintbrush.

4 When all the pictures are in place, leave it to dry.

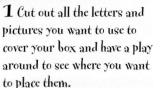

5 Paint over the entire surface with a coat of the glue and water solution and leave it to dry. Repeat this process until the edges of the pictures feel smooth, leaving the glue to dry completely between coats.

Sparkly Fairy Dust

When you are making special fairy wishes, a pinch of fairy dust sprinkled in the air will encourage the fairies to work their magic to help make your wish come true. Put 1 teaspoon of dried lavender, 1½ teaspoons of multi-colored glitter and ½ teaspoon of dried rosemary into a clear bottle or container with a lid. Put the lid on and shake well. Make your wish while sprinkling a tiny pinch of fairy dust.

Treasure Chest

Go on a treasure hunt and see how many pieces of fairy treasure you can find. Then make a treasure chest to keep them safe. This chest is quite tricky to make, so ask an adult to help you follow the instructions.

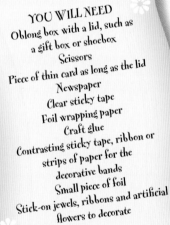

YOU WILL NEED
Oblong box with a lid, such as a gift box or shoebox
Scissors
Piece of thin card as long as the lid
Newspaper
Clear sticky tape
Foil wrapping paper
Craft glue
Contrasting sticky tape, ribbon or strips of paper for the decorative bands
Small piece of foil
Stick-on jewels, ribbons and artificial flowers to decorate

1 Measure the lid of your box and ask an adult to cut a piece of card and a piece of paper to the same length and twice the width. Fold the long edge of the card over one side of the box and tape it securely on the inside of the lid. Curve the piece of card over the top of the lid and tape it to the other side in the same way.

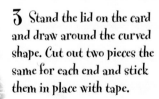

2 Scrunch up some sheets of newspaper and use them to fill up the gap between the curved card and the lid.

3 Stand the lid on the card and draw around the curved shape. Cut out two pieces the same for each end and stick them in place with tape.

4 Cover the sides of the box with foil paper, using glue to stick it in place. Fold the paper neatly over the top edges of the box and glue it down.

5 To cover the ends of the lid, stand the lid on the wrong side of the foil paper, draw around the curved ends and add an extra 1cm (½in) all round. Cut a piece of foil paper to this size for both ends. Make 1cm (½in) snips at intervals around the curved edge of the paper, then glue the paper onto the end of the lid, folding the straight edge to the inside of the lid and sticking the snipped edge onto the curved lid.

6 Use the foil paper that you cut out in step 1. Stick it onto the curved lid, folding and sticking the long edges to the inside of the lid.

7 Stick two vertical strips of colored sticky tape, ribbon or paper up the front of the box, about 8cm (3in) in from each end. Stick another two strips up the back of the box. Then stick another two pieces over the lid.

8 Cut out a keyhole shape from the foil wrapping paper and stick it on the front of your box in the center.

9 Decorate the chest with stick-on jewels, ribbons and artificial flowers.

Keepsake Pot

This is a sweet little pot to make for your dressing table to keep your trinkets safe. When it's dry, you can paint it and stick things on it such as jewels or shells.

1 Working on a wipe-clean surface, take a lump of clay the size of a tennis ball and roll it into a smooth, even ball. Press your thumb halfway into the center of the ball.

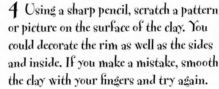

YOU WILL NEED
Air-dry clay
Sharp pencil
Paints and paintbrush

2 Pinch the sides of the pot between your fingers and thumbs, turning it as you work to keep the clay an even thickness all round. Keep doing this until the clay is about as thick as your finger.

3 Smooth the surface of the clay with your fingers and make sure the base is flat so that your pot will sit without wobbling.

4 Using a sharp pencil, scratch a pattern or picture on the surface of the clay. You could decorate the rim as well as the sides and inside. If you make a mistake, smooth the clay with your fingers and try again.

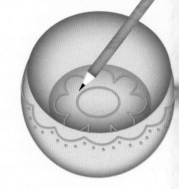

5 When you're happy with your pot, leave it to dry thoroughly. This might take a couple of days – check the instructions on the packaging.

6 Paint the pot in your chosen colors, leaving each color to dry before painting the next color.

Pen Pot

Fairies are very inventive and good at making useful items out of things you would usually throw away. Here's how to make a handy pen pot with an empty toilet or kitchen tube.

YOU WILL NEED
Empty toilet or kitchen roll tube
Piece of card and pencil
Scissors
Pretty fabric or paper, 15 x 25cm (6 x 10in)
Craft glue
15cm (6in) feather trim
Glitter

1 Stand the tube on the piece of card and draw around its base with a pencil. Ask an adult to help cut the circle out of the card. This will be the pen pot's base.

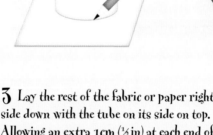

2 Glue the card circle onto one end of the fabric or paper. Ask an adult to cut it out with an extra 5mm (¼in) all round for the overlap. Make snips all the way around the overlap about 5mm (¼in) apart. Apply glue around the edge of the card and stick the overlap in place.

3 Lay the rest of the fabric or paper right side down with the tube on its side on top. Allowing an extra 1cm (½in) at each end of the tube for the overlap, cut the fabric or paper to length.

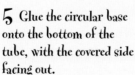

Template

4 Apply glue to one edge of the fabric or paper and stick it onto the tube. Roll the tube up and stick the other side of the fabric or paper in place. Snip into the overlap at each end of the tube and glue it to the inside.

5 Glue the circular base onto the bottom of the tube, with the covered side facing out.

6 Glue the feather trim around the top of the tube.

7 Trace the star template above onto a piece of card and cut it out. Cover it with glue and scatter glitter over it. Glue this to the front of the pot.

Blooming Garden

The garden is a fairy's playground. They love to flutter through the flowers, skip around tall blades of grass and slide down leaves. Make your own miniature fairy garden, using leaves, petals, twigs, acorns and anything else you can find in the garden or park.

YOU WILL NEED

Foil dish, such as a small baking tray or shoebox lid lined with plastic or kitchen foil
Moist earth or potting compost
Selection of treasures from the garden, such as moss, acorns, leaves or little cuttings from shrubs, twigs, little flowers such as daisies, and pretty pebbles
Scissors
Kitchen foil
Craft glue
Plasticine or sticky tack
Cocktail sticks
Green garden string or wool
Hair grips
Pretty buttons
Dolls' house table and chairs and a cocktail umbrella

1 Spread a thin layer of earth over your tray.

2 Pile a few pebbles in one corner to make a rockery.

3 Pick out some flat pebbles to make a winding pathway of stepping stones around your garden.

4 Make a little mound at one end and cover it with moss.

5 Cut a fishpond out of kitchen foil, then cut out some orange fish and stick them on the pond. Or use a little foil dish such as a tart or pie tray and fill it with water to make a pool.

6 Glue leaves onto twigs to make little trees. Use plasticine or sticky tack to hold them in place, then cover it with earth.

7 Make an allotment area or vegetable patch. Edge it with twigs and make tomatoes and cabbages out of plasticine. You could use cocktail sticks for runner bean canes, and wind green garden string or wool around them.

8 Add color with the flowers and shrub cuttings, pushing them into the earth. Daisies work well, or any other little flowers or sprigs of honeysuckle or jasmine.

9 If you can't find any flowers to use, put hair grips through the holes in pretty buttons and then push them into your mossy bank.

10 Use acorns to make little fairy seats. Or, use a dolls' house table and chairs, if you have one, and a cocktail umbrella for a parasol.

Butterfly Garden

Fairies and butterflies enjoy fluttering around together, so ask an adult if you can create a special area in your garden that will encourage lots of pretty butterflies to visit. Most butterflies like the sunshine, so it's a good idea to position your butterfly garden in a sunny, sheltered spot. Choose flowers that are brightly colored with a strong scent. Bluebells, lavender and poppies are all flowers that butterflies love.

Fancy Flowerpots

Why not decorate some terracotta plant pots to grow some flowers and herbs? Paint them in pretty colors and then decorate them.

1 Use your paintbrush to paint the flowerpots in any color you wish. Leave to dry thoroughly, for at least one day.

2 Using the ladybird template on page 79 and the fairy template on page 44, trace your chosen design onto a piece of card and ask an adult to cut them out to make templates. Draw around the templates with a pencil onto your painted pots. Then color in the shapes with other colors of acrylic paint.

3 Glue shells or flat pebbles onto your pots in a pretty shape. Draw the design in pencil first and then stick the shells or pebbles in place.

4 Glue gems and jewels onto your plant pots in the shape of a star and add a straight line to make a wand.

YOU WILL NEED
Paintbrush
Small terracotta plant pots
Selection of water-based acrylic paints in different colors
Tracing paper and pencil
Piece of card
Scissors
Shells or pebbles to decorate
Craft glue
Stick-on gems and jewels

Plate House

Use woodland finds from the garden to build a fairy house on a paper plate or piece of card. Collect little twigs, leaves, grass and flower petals.

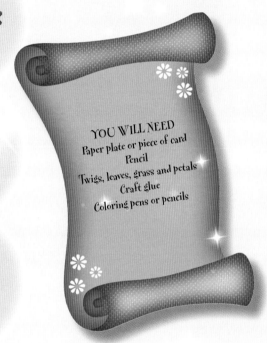

YOU WILL NEED
Paper plate or piece of card
Pencil
Twigs, leaves, grass and petals
Craft glue
Coloring pens or pencils

1 Imagine what your fairy house is going to look like and sketch the outline on the paper plate or piece of card with a pencil.

2 Start building the outline of the house with twigs. Break or cut them to length and glue them onto the plate or card.

3 Break off small pieces of twigs and use them to make the window and door frames. Fill in the rest of the door with twigs, too.

4 Use flower petals or leaves for the roof of the house, cutting them to shape to fit within the drawn shape.

5 Decorate the ground in front of the house by gluing pieces of grass and flower petals in place.

6 With your coloring pens or pencils, draw curtains inside the windows, a chimney on the roof and flowers around the door.

Fun Fairy Swing

Fairies love to feel the wind in their hair and sail through the air. Make a little swing for your fairy friends and maybe a fairy will come to play in your garden.

YOU WILL NEED
Twigs
Craft glue
Plasticine or sticky tack
Garden string

1 Break or cut four twigs to about 8cm (3in) long. Take one pair and cross them over each other near the top. Glue them together at the point where they meet. Do the same for the other pair, making sure they cross at the same point as the first two.

2 Make four little balls of plasticine or sticky tack and stick one ball onto the end of each twig, furthest from the cross. These will help to anchor your swing frame to the surface. Position the two pairs of twigs side by side, about 4cm (1½ in) apart.

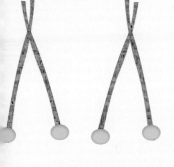

3 Cut or break another twig long enough to sit across the two crosses to make the top bar of the frame. Balance it in place.

4 For the swing seat, make a little bundle of twigs 2.5cm (1in) long and tie them together tightly with string at both ends of the bundle.

5 Cut two lengths of string 15cm (6in) long and tie one end of each to the string at each end of the bundle. Then work out how high you want your swing seat to be and tie the ends of the string around the top bar of the swing frame. Trim off the ends.

6 Why don't you put your fairy swing in your fairy garden (see page 88).

Felt Fairies

YOU WILL NEED
Tracing paper and pencil
Card for template
Scissors
Colorful felt
Fabric-marker pen
Lace, ribbon and jewels
to decorate
Craft glue

Felt fairies are fun and easy to make. You can decorate your fairy and glue it onto paper or a piece of fabric to make a picture, or just hang it up as a decoration. Make several in lots of different colors and hang them from string like bunting.

1 Trace the outline shown here onto a piece of card and ask an adult to help cut it out to make a template. Position the template on a piece of felt and draw around it with a pencil or fabric-marker pen. Ask an adult to cut out the fairy from the felt.

2 You can leave your fairy plain, especially if you are going to make several in different colors, or decorate her as you wish. You could cut decorative details from other colors of felt and stick them on, add lace to the wings, or trim her dress with some ribbon and jewels. Then, decide what you are going to do with your fairy.

Templates

Enlarge these templates to the size you want your fairy to be.

Felt-Fairy Decoration

Felt-Fairy Picture

Cheat's Appliqué

Felt-Fairy Bunting

Here are some fun ideas:

Felt-Fairy Picture
Glue the felt fairy onto a piece of paper and draw a picture around her using colored pens, pencils or crayons.

Cheat's Appliqué
Ask an adult to help cut a square of pretty fabric using pinking shears and glue the fairy onto the center of the square. Frame it to make a lovely present.

Felt-Fairy Decoration
Cut a length of ribbon or embroidery thread which is long enough to hook over whatever you want to hang the fairy on – a doorknob, for example. Glue the ends together onto the back of the fairy.

Felt-Fairy Bunting
Cut lengths of embroidery thread about 10cm (4in) long and glue the ends together onto the back of each fairy. Thread the loops onto a piece of string or tape.

Fairy Puppet

Make fairy puppets in different colors, so you can put on your own fairy play. You could make a red fairy like Ruby Rose, a blue one like Bluebell Sapphire, a purple one like Violet Amethyst and so on.

YOU WILL NEED

Pipe cleaner for the body and arms
Bendy straw
Craft glue
Small Styrofoam ball for the head
Tracing paper, pencil and card
Scissors
Colored felt or other fabric for the skirt, 10 x 10cm (4 x 4in)
Pinking shears
Ribbon or lace to trim the skirt
Lengths of ribbon for wings
Embroidery thread for the hair
Colored pens

1 Hold the pipe cleaner horizontally behind the bendy straw, just where the bend is. Take one side of the pipe cleaner and wrap it around the straw once. Repeat with the other side. Continue wrapping the pipe cleaner around the straw to about 1cm (⅓ in) from the top, alternating sides. The ends of the pipe cleaners that are left will be the fairy's arms.

2 Apply glue to the end of the straw and push the Styrofoam ball onto it.

3 Trace the skirt template onto a piece of card and cut it out to make a card template.

Template

Enlarge this template to fit as a skirt around the straw. You could give your fairy a long or short skirt.

4 Lay the template on the wrong side of your fabric and draw around it. Ask an adult to help cut it out with pinking shears. If you wish, trim the skirt with ribbon or lace, gluing it in place. Then attach the skirt to the fairy's body by wrapping it around her waist and gluing it onto the pipe cleaner. Glue the edges of the skirt together neatly at the back, folding the top edge under.

5 Cut two pieces of ribbon for the wings. Cut the pieces at an angle, as shown, to make wing shapes. Glue the short edges to the back of the fairy.

6 Cut a few equal lengths of embroidery thread for the fairy's hair and glue it onto her head.

7 Use the colored pens to draw on her eyes, nose and mouth.

Saltdough Decorations

These lovely decorations can be made out of air-dry clay or saltdough, which you can make yourself.

1 Mix the flour and salt in a bowl. Add the water gradually, mixing it well to form a soft dough. Remove from the bowl and knead with your hands for 10 minutes to create a smooth texture. Leave the dough to rest for about 20 minutes before rolling it out.

2 On a floured surface, roll out the dough until it is about 5mm (¼in) thick.

3 Use the fairy cookie cutters to cut out different shapes. Place them on a baking tray.

4 Using the wooden skewer, make a little hole in the top of each decoration so you can thread fine ribbon or thread through it to hang it up. You can also decorate the shapes by making an indented pattern on them with the wooden skewer.

5 You can either leave the shapes to air dry, which can take up to two days, or ask an adult to bake them for about 4 hours in the oven on the lowest setting. Turn them halfway through the cooking time.

6 When the shapes are dry and cool, paint them in different colors and glue on some pretty jewels.

7 Thread ribbon or thread through the holes and knot the ends together so that you can hang up your decorations.

Fridge Magnets

Make the fairy shapes into fridge magnets instead of hanging decorations. To do this, don't punch holes in the shapes. Instead, glue a magnet onto the back of each decoration when the shapes are finished.

Flowery Collage

Make a collage of lots of pretty fairies fluttering through the air, using flower petals and daisies collected from the garden. Look at the shapes of the different petals you have found and let your imagination take over.

YOU WILL NEED
Tracing paper and pencil
Piece of paper
Selection of flower petals
Craft glue
Coloring pens, pencils
or crayons
Glitter

Here are some ideas for creating your collage:

1 Trace the fairy template on page 44 or the finished fairies in the picture below onto a piece of paper. Take the piece of paper and then start to build up your collage by gluing on the flower petals. Start with the fairy's skirt. Use a large petal, such as a rose, poppy or pansy, or overlap two or three for a full skirt.

2 You can make a different style of skirt using lots of long, thin petals and gluing them in a fanned-out shape to make a tutu. Zinnia, gerbera, chrysanthemum or long daisy petals work well.

3 Use rounded petals, such as rose, primrose or buttercup, for fairy wings.

4 For the fairy's body, either use a smaller petal, such as a buttercup, or use a few daisy, chrysanthemum or dandelion petals laid side by side.

5 Single daisy, chrysanthemum or dandelion petals make good arms and legs. Or you can draw them with colored pens or pencils if you wish.

6 Draw the fairy's heads and wands with pens, pencils or crayons, using glitter for the wand.

Cut-Out Fairy

Make a basic fairy shape out of card, then trace the dresses and shoes onto stiff paper or thin card and have fun coloring them in and decorating them with glitter. You can make as many different outfits as you like. Then you can dress your fairy in all her pretty new clothes.

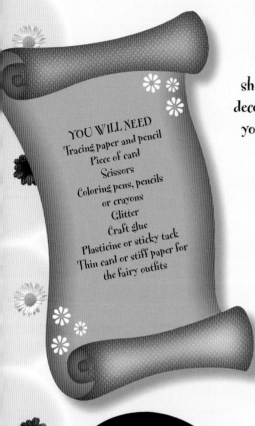

YOU WILL NEED
Tracing paper and pencil
Piece of card
Scissors
Coloring pens, pencils
or crayons
Glitter
Craft glue
Plasticine or sticky tack
Thin card or stiff paper for
the fairy outfits

1 Trace the fairy onto a piece of card and ask and adult to help you cut her out.

2 Color in her hair and wings as you wish, perhaps adding glitter to her wings using a little glue.

3 Fold the base under her feet, so that she stands up. You can always stick a little piece of plasticine or sticky tack under the base to hold her in place.

4 Trace the dresses and shoes, including the tabs, onto the thin card or paper and cut them out.

5 Color them in and decorate with glitter.

6 You can then dress your fairy in whichever outfit you choose, folding the tabs over her shoulders to hold it in place.

Templates

Enlarge these templates of the fairy figure and her clothes to the size you would like your cut-out fairy to be.

Rag Doll Fairy

Rag dolls are easy to make using scraps of old fabric. Use soft cotton fabric in pretty fairy colors – you could use an old pink shirt or a white or cream pillowcase.

YOU WILL NEED
Scissors
Pair of old sheer tights
Square of fabric, about 50 x 50cm (20 x 20in)
6–7 pieces of tulle ribbon or strips of pretty fabric, about 30cm (12in) long
30cm (12in) wire-edged ribbon
Fabric glue
Tinsel pipe cleaner
Fabric pen

1 Ask an adult to help cut up the tights into pieces about 5cm (2in) long.

2 Lay the fabric wrong side up on your work surface and place a few pieces of the tights in the center.

3 Lift up the edges of the fabric and take hold of the middle, just above where the tights are. Flip the fabric over. The 'ball' shape will be the fairy's head. Still holding the fabric tightly with one hand, push more pieces of tights in with your finger until the head is the size you want.

4 Wind a tulle ribbon or strip of fabric tightly under the head a couple of times and knot it securely. Then tie the ends in a bow around her neck.

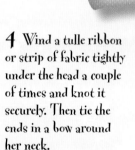

5 Push some more pieces of tights under the fabric to form the fairy's body – try to make it an oval rather than round shape. Then tie another tulle ribbon or strip of fabric around to form her waist, letting the ends fall down as another layer of her dress.

6 Tie on the other tulle ribbons or fabric strips so that the ends hang down all round the fairy to make her skirt nice and full.

7 Take the wire-edged ribbon and bring both ends into the center to create two loops. Glue the ends in place and arrange the ribbon loops into a flat bow shape to make the wings. Glue the wings onto the back of the fairy.

8 Twist the pipe cleaner into a circle, twisting it around itself to make a rope-like crown for the fairy, and glue it onto her head.

9 Draw the eyes, nose and mouth onto your fairy using the fabric pen.

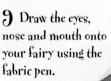

Peg Doll Fairy

Make a fairy peg doll using an old-fashioned clothes peg for the body and some pretty fabric and sparkly tulle for the fairy's dress.

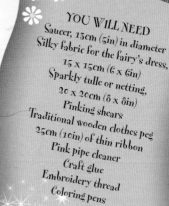

YOU WILL NEED
Saucer, 13cm (5in) in diameter
Silky fabric for the fairy's dress,
15 x 15cm (6 x 6in)
Sparkly tulle or netting,
20 x 20cm (8 x 8in)
Pinking shears
Traditional wooden clothes peg
25cm (10in) of thin ribbon
Pink pipe cleaner
Craft glue
Embroidery thread
Coloring pens

1 Draw a circle with a 13cm (5in) diameter on the wrong side of both pieces of fabric, using a saucer. Ask an adult to help cut out the circles of fabric using the pinking shears.

2 Fold both circles of fabric in half and then in half again. Ask an adult to help cut off the center points about 5mm (¼in) down.

3 Open out the circles of fabric to reveal a hole in the center of each. Put the silky fabric right side out over the top of the peg (the fairy's head). Do the same with the tulle.

4 Tie the ribbon in a bow around the fairy's waist, about 2.5cm (1in) down from the head. Make sure the bow is at the back of the fairy with a 'leg' at each side.

5 Position the center of the pipe cleaner on the front of her neck and cross the ends around each other at the back. Bring her pipe-cleaner arms back to the front and curl the ends in to make hands.

6 For the wings, make a paper template as follows: first draw a triangle. Cut out the paper triangle, then cut off the point about 1cm (½in) in. Using this template, ask your adult to cut out two wing shapes from the left-over tulle. Glue them onto the back of the fairy.

7 Cut lengths of embroidery thread for the fairy's hair and glue them onto her head. Draw on her eyes, nose and mouth.